The Photocopiable

FOUR RULES

OF

NUMBER

Reinforcement Book

by Peter Bell

Published by
"TOPICAL RESOURCES"

The Photocopiable Four Rules of Number Reinforcement Book is available from all good Educational Bookshops and by mail order from: Topical Resources, P.O.Box 329, Broughton, Preston, Lancashire PR3 5LT. Topical Resources publishes a range of Educational Materials for use in Primary Schools and Pre-School Nurseries and Playgroups.

For latest catalogue Tel/Fax. 01772 863158

Copyright © 1996 Topical Resources
Printed in Great Britain for "Topical Resources", Publishers of Educational Materials, P.O. Box 329, Broughton, Preston PR3 5LT (Telephone 01772 863158) by T.Snape & Company Ltd., Boltons Court, Preston.
Typeset by "Topical Resources".
First Published January 1996. Reprint February 1997. 2nd Reprint September 1997.
ISBN 1 872977 21 9

INTRODUCTION

The "Photocopiable Four Rules of Number Reinforcement Book" can be used by busy Key Stage 2 teachers in a number of different ways. Examples include:

(1) Teaching younger children the basic skills of addition, subtraction, multiplication and division.

(2) To reinforce the work of older pupils that have not grasped the basic four rules of number skills at an earlier stage.

(3) To provide additional material to supplement existing maths schemes which don't provide quite enough practice in simple computational skills.

(4) As a quick way to diagnose the exact level a new pupil is working at in number work if he/she transfers from another school mid-year.

(5) To provide a relatively instant activity for a supply teacher or headteacher required to cover for a Key Stage 2 class at short notice.

The book contains 86 carefully graded exercises from addition of tens and units to multiplication and division of decimals. The first 60 exercises deal with simple addition , subtraction, multiplication and division. Small steps are taken from addition of tens and units through to division of hundred, tens and units with carrying figures and remainders. Each step has three parallel exercises with no new skills introduced. If pupils cope easily with the first exercise on a new level then the teacher may well decide to move pupils to the next level without further practice. However, if required, there are two additional exercises available at each level.

Exercises 61 to 70 are Revision Exercises which require pupils to use all four rules of number work in one lesson . The are also introduced to questions which are set out horizontally and use some text. These exercises can be used to reinforce the work previously taught, pick up on individual problems and encourage more able pupils to work with speed and accuracy. These exercises can be used with whole class groups by setting different targets for children of different abilities.

Exercises 71 to 78 introduce long multiplication. Again the teacher will use professional judgement concerning how many of these exercises individual children will attempt.

Exercises 79 to 86 introduce decimals and place value for the first time. Pupils will need to be taught how to set out these questions accurately considering the position of the decimal point. Questions are also introduced on money, length, weight, capacity and time where pupils are required to change from one unit of measure to another. Again, these exercises can be used with whole class groups by setting different targets for children of different abilities.

The answers for all the exercises can be found at the back of the book.

A simple diagnostic test has been provided at the front of the book instead of a contents page. The test clearly shows how the exercises develop and where they can be found. The test could be used to check the progress of a class new to the teacher at the beginning of the acadenic year, or for assessing individual pupils that transfer from other schools.

Diagnostic Test Page 1

Name _____

(1)
```
 T U
 2 1
+2 8
────
```

(2)
```
 T U
 2 2
+2 7
────
```

(3)
```
 T U
 2 3
+2 5
────
```

Addition of Tens and Units with no carrying.

Exercises 1 - 3

(4)
```
 T U
 2 1
+1 9
────
```

(5)
```
 T U
 2 2
+1 8
────
```

(6)
```
 T U
 2 3
+1 7
────
```

Addition of Tens and Units with carrying.

Exercices 4 - 6

(7)
```
 H T U
 2 4 5
+1 4 3
──────
```

(8)
```
 H T U
 2 1 8
+1 8 1
──────
```

(9)
```
 H T U
 2 7 6
+1 2 3
──────
```

Addition of Hundreds, Tens and Units with no carrying.

Exercises 7 - 9

(10)
```
 H T U
 1 2 3
+1 1 7
──────
```

(11)
```
 H T U
 1 2 5
+1 1 5
──────
```

(12)
```
 H T U
 1 2 6
+1 3 4
──────
```

Addition of Hundreds, Tens and Units with carrying.

Exercises 10 - 12

(13)
```
 T U
 2 1
-1 1
────
```

(14)
```
 T U
 2 2
-1 0
────
```

(15)
```
 T U
 2 3
-1 2
────
```

Subtraction of Tens and Units with no carrying.

Exercises 13 - 15

(16)
```
 T U
 2 3
-1 4
────
```

(17)
```
 T U
 2 4
-1 7
────
```

(18)
```
 T U
 2 5
-1 7
────
```

Subtraction of Tens and units with carrying.

Exercises 16 - 18

(19)
```
 H T U
 2 2 4
-1 1 3
──────
```

(20)
```
 H T U
 2 2 9
-1 1 6
──────
```

(21)
```
 H T U
 2 2 8
-1 1 7
──────
```

Subtraction of Hundreds, Tens and Units with no carrying.

Exercises 19 - 21

Name_____

(22)
```
H  T  U
   2  3  5
-  1  1  7
_____
```

(23)
```
H  T  U
   2  1  7
-  1  0  9
_____
```

(24)
```
H  T  U
   2  6  8
-  2  2  9
_____
```

Subtraction of Hundreds, Tens and Units with carrying.

Exercises 22 - 24

(25)
```
T  U
1  2
x  2
____
____
```

(26)
```
T  U
1  3
x  2
____
____
```

(27)
```
T  U
1  4
x  2
____
____
```

Multiplication of Tens and Units with no carrying.

Exercises 25 - 27

(28)
```
T  U
2  5
x  2
____
____
```

(29)
```
T  U
2  6
x  2
____
____
```

(30)
```
T  U
2  7
x  2
____
____
```

Multiplication of Tens and Units with carrying.

Exercises 28 - 30

(31)
```
H  T  U
1  4  3
   x  2
_____
_____
```

(32)
```
H  T  U
1  3  4
   x  2
_____
_____
```

(33)
```
H  T  U
1  3  0
   x  2
_____
_____
```

Multiplication of Hundreds, Tens and Units with no carrying.

Exercises 31 - 33

(34)
```
H  T  U
2  2  5
   x  2
_____
_____
```

(35)
```
H  T  U
2  3  7
   x  2
_____
_____
```

(36)
```
H  T  U
2  0  9
   x  2
_____
_____
```

Multiplication of Hundreds, Tens and Units with carrying.

Exercises 34 - 36

(37)
```
T  U

2 | 0  2
```

(38)
```
T  U

2 | 0  4
```

(39)
```
T  U

2 | 0  6
```

Division of Tens and Units with no carrying.
Exercises 37 - 39

(40)
```
H  T  U

2 | 2  0  0
```

(41)
```
H  T  U

2 | 2  2  2
```

(42)
```
H  T  U

2 | 2  2  4
```

Division of Hundreds, Tens and Units with no carrying.
Exercises 40 - 42

Diagnostic Test Page 3   **Name**_____

(43) T U 2 ⟌ 2 3	**(44)** T U 2 ⟌ 2 5	**(45)** T U 2 ⟌ 2 7	Division of Tens and Units with a remainder. Exercises 43 - 45
(46) H T U 2 ⟌ 2 2 3	**(47)** H T U 2 ⟌ 2 4 5	**(48)** H T U 2 ⟌ 2 6 7	Division of Hundreds, Tens and Units with a remainder. Exercises 46 - 48
(49) T U 2 ⟌ 3 6	**(50)** T U 2 ⟌ 5 4	**(51)** T U 2 ⟌ 7 2	Division of Tens and Units with carrying. Exercises 49 - 51
(52) H T U 2 ⟌ 2 1 6	**(53)** H T U 2 ⟌ 2 1 8	**(54)** H T U 2 ⟌ 2 3 2	Division of Hundreds, Tens and Units with carrying. Exercises 52 - 54
(55) T U 2 ⟌ 3 3	**(56)** T U 2 ⟌ 3 5	**(57)** T U 2 ⟌ 3 7	Division of Tens and Units with a remainder. Exercises 55 - 57
(58) H T U 2 ⟌ 1 7 9	**(59)** H T U 2 ⟌ 5 3 1	**(60)** H T U 2 ⟌ 7 1 9	Division of Hundreds, Tens and Units with a remainder. Exercises 58 - 60

(61) Add together 17, 57 and 44. **(62)** What is 566 take away 345? **(63)** What is 266 times 5? **(64)** Divide 636 by 6.	Revision of all four rules of number. Exercises 61 - 70

(65) 1 4 3 x 3 2 ‾‾‾‾‾‾ ‾‾‾‾‾‾	**(66)** 1 3 4 x 2 4 ‾‾‾‾‾‾ ‾‾‾‾‾‾	**(67)** 1 3 0 x 5 6 ‾‾‾‾‾‾ ‾‾‾‾‾‾	Long Multiplication. Exercises

(68) 1 . 19 + 232 . 1 + 6 . 4 **(69)** 2m + 80 cm. Give your answer in m and cm. **(70)** 2 litres - 1200ml. Give your answer in ml.	Decimals and Place Value. Exercises

Exercise 1

Add tens and units.

(1)
```
T U
2 1
+2 8
___
```

(2)
```
T U
2 2
+2 7
___
```

(3)
```
T U
2 3
+2 5
___
```

(4)
```
T U
2 4
+2 4
___
```

(5)
```
T U
2 5
+3 1
___
```

(6)
```
T U
2 6
+3 2
___
```

(7)
```
T U
2 7
+4 1
___
```

(8)
```
T U
2 8
+4 0
___
```

(9)
```
T U
3 0
+2 1
___
```

(10)
```
T U
3 1
+2 2
___
```

(11)
```
T U
3 2
+2 3
___
```

(12)
```
T U
3 3
+2 4
___
```

(13)
```
T U
3 4
+3 1
___
```

(14)
```
T U
3 5
+3 2
___
```

(15)
```
T U
3 6
+3 3
___
```

(16)
```
T U
3 7
+3 0
___
```

Exercise 2

Always add the units first!

(1)
```
T U
3 8
+4 1
___
```

(2)
```
T U
3 9
+2 0
___
```

(3)
```
T U
4 0
+2 2
___
```

(4)
```
T U
4 1
+2 3
___
```

(5)
```
T U
4 2
+4 1
___
```

(6)
```
T U
4 3
+4 2
___
```

(7)
```
T U
4 4
+4 3
___
```

(8)
```
T U
4 5
+2 1
___
```

(9)
```
T U
5 0
+4 3
___
```

(10)
```
T U
5 1
+4 4
___
```

(11)
```
T U
5 2
+3 5
___
```

(12)
```
T U
5 3
+3 6
___
```

(13)
```
T U
2 3
+2 5
___
```

(14)
```
T U
2 3
+2 5
___
```

(15)
```
T U
2 3
+2 5
___
```

(16)
```
T U
2 3
+2 5
___
```

Exercise 3

Remember! Add the units first.

(1)
```
 T U
 5 4
+2 1
────
```

(2)
```
 T U
 5 5
+2 2
────
```

(3)
```
 T U
 5 6
+2 3
────
```

(4)
```
 T U
 5 7
+2 0
────
```

(5)
```
 T U
 5 8
+4 1
────
```

(6)
```
 T U
 5 9
+4 0
────
```

(7)
```
 T U
 6 0
+3 8
────
```

(8)
```
 T U
 6 1
+3 3
────
```

(9)
```
 T U
 6 2
+3 7
────
```

(10)
```
 T U
 6 3
+3 4
────
```

(11)
```
 T U
 6 4
+3 2
────
```

(12)
```
 T U
 6 5
+3 4
────
```

(13)
```
 T U
 7 0
+2 6
────
```

(14)
```
 T U
 7 1
+2 8
────
```

(15)
```
 T U
 8 3
+1 6
────
```

(16)
```
 T U
 8 4
+1 2
────
```

Exercise 4

Add tens and units.

(1)
```
 T U
 2 1
+1 9
────
```

(2)
```
 T U
 2 2
+1 8
────
```

(3)
```
 T U
 2 3
+1 7
────
```

(4)
```
 T U
 2 4
+1 6
────
```

(5)
```
 T U
 2 5
+2 5
────
```

(6)
```
 T U
 2 6
+2 4
────
```

(7)
```
 T U
 2 7
+2 4
────
```

(8)
```
 T U
 2 8
+2 5
────
```

(9)
```
 T U
 2 9
+3 1
────
```

(10)
```
 T U
 3 9
+3 2
────
```

(11)
```
 T U
 3 1
+3 9
────
```

(12)
```
 T U
 3 2
+4 9
────
```

(13)
```
 T U
 3 3
+4 8
────
```

(14)
```
 T U
 3 4
+3 9
────
```

(15)
```
 T U
 3 5
+3 8
────
```

(16)
```
 T U
 3 6
+3 9
────
```

Exercise 6

Do all the units on this page have a number to carry?

(1) T U
   5 8
+4 9
___

(2) T U
   5 9
+5 1
___

(3) T U
   6 3
+5 2
___

(4) T U
   6 4
+5 3
___

(5) T U
   6 5
+4 5
___

(6) T U
   6 6
+4 6
___

(7) T U
   6 7
+4 7
___

(8) T U
   6 8
+4 8
___

(9) T U
   6 9
+4 5
___

(10) T U
   7 3
+4 6
___

(11) T U
   7 4
+4 7
___

(12) T U
   7 5
+3 5
___

(13) T U
   7 6
+3 5
___

(14) T U
   7 7
+3 7
___

(15) T U
   7 8
+4 5
___

(16) T U
   7 9
+4 8
___

Exercise 5

10 or more in the units? Carry to the tens column.

(1) T U
   3 7
+4 3
___

(2) T U
   3 8
+4 6
___

(3) T U
   3 9
+4 4
___

(4) T U
   4 2
+4 9
___

(5) T U
   4 3
+2 7
___

(6) T U
   4 4
+2 8
___

(7) T U
   4 5
+2 9
___

(8) T U
   4 6
+2 8
___

(9) T U
   4 7
+5 5
___

(10) T U
   4 8
+5 3
___

(11) T U
   4 9
+5 5
___

(12) T U
   5 3
+5 8
___

(13) T U
   5 4
+4 7
___

(14) T U
   5 5
+4 8
___

(15) T U
   5 6
+6 7
___

(16) T U
   5 7
+6 8
___

Exercise 8 — Remember, start with the units!

(1)
```
H T U
4 4 4
+ 2 1 5
-------
```

(2)
```
H T U
4 2 6
+ 3 6 3
-------
```

(3)
```
H T U
4 4 8
+ 4 0 1
-------
```

(4)
```
H T U
4 4 5
+ 3 2 4
-------
```

(5)
```
H T U
4 7 6
+ 5 2 1
-------
```

(6)
```
H T U
4 3 2
+ 2 6 7
-------
```

(7)
```
H T U
5 2 7
+ 2 1 0
-------
```

(8)
```
H T U
5 5 3
+ 3 2 6
-------
```

(9)
```
H T U
5 5 5
+ 4 4 1
-------
```

(10)
```
H T U
5 6 7
+ 4 2 2
-------
```

(11)
```
H T U
5 8 1
+ 3 1 4
-------
```

(12)
```
H T U
5 7 8
+ 4 2 1
-------
```

Exercise 7 — Add hundreds, tens and units.

(1)
```
H T U
2 4 5
+ 1 4 3
-------
```

(2)
```
H T U
2 1 8
+ 1 8 1
-------
```

(3)
```
H T U
2 7 6
+ 1 2 3
-------
```

(4)
```
H T U
2 3 3
+ 6 1 5
-------
```

(5)
```
H T U
2 7 1
+ 7 1 4
-------
```

(6)
```
H T U
2 2 6
+ 6 6 3
-------
```

(7)
```
H T U
3 1 0
+ 4 4 6
-------
```

(8)
```
H T U
3 2 3
+ 4 3 6
-------
```

(9)
```
H T U
3 6 8
+ 5 2 1
-------
```

(10)
```
H T U
3 4 1
+ 2 3 6
-------
```

(11)
```
H T U
3 5 2
+ 2 4 7
-------
```

(12)
```
H T U
3 7 0
+ 2 1 9
-------
```

(1)
```
H T U
6 2 2
+ 3 1 2
───────
```

(2)
```
H T U
6 3 5
+ 3 1 3
───────
```

(3)
```
H T U
6 4 2
+ 3 5 4
───────
```

(4)
```
H T U
6 5 6
+ 2 2 3
───────
```

(5)
```
H T U
6 7 6
+ 2 1 3
───────
```

(6)
```
H T U
6 0 2
+ 3 9 1
───────
```

(7)
```
H T U
7 3 5
+ 2 4 4
───────
```

(8)
```
H T U
7 2 4
+ 2 1 2
───────
```

(9)
```
H T U
7 5 8
+ 2 0 1
───────
```

(10)
```
H T U
7 9 6
+ 2 0 3
───────
```

(11)
```
H T U
7 7 7
+ 2 1 0
───────
```

(12)
```
H T U
7 3 6
+ 2 4 2
───────
```

Exercise 10

10 or more in the units?
Carry to the tens column.

(1)
```
H T U
1 2 3
+ 1 1 7
───────
```

(2)
```
H T U
1 2 5
+ 1 1 5
───────
```

(3)
```
H T U
1 2 6
+ 1 3 4
───────
```

(4)
```
H T U
1 4 4
+ 1 2 6
───────
```

(5)
```
H T U
1 5 4
+ 1 1 7
───────
```

(6)
```
H T U
1 2 6
+ 1 1 5
───────
```

(7)
```
H T U
2 3 7
+ 2 2 4
───────
```

(8)
```
H T U
2 2 8
+ 2 1 7
───────
```

(9)
```
H T U
2 3 6
+ 2 1 7
───────
```

(10)
```
H T U
2 4 7
+ 1 1 6
───────
```

(11)
```
H T U
2 4 8
+ 1 1 8
───────
```

(12)
```
H T U
2 4 9
+ 1 1 5
───────
```

Exercise 11

(1)
```
H T U
3 2 4
+ 1 8 6
───────
```

(2)
```
H T U
3 6 2
+ 1 4 8
───────
```

(3)
```
H T U
3 8 5
+ 1 2 5
───────
```

(4)
```
H T U
3 4 6
+ 1 6 5
───────
```

(5)
```
H T U
3 5 4
+ 1 7 7
───────
```

(6)
```
H T U
3 8 2
+ 1 3 9
───────
```

(7)
```
H T U
4 7 8
+ 1 3 5
───────
```

(8)
```
H T U
4 6 5
+ 1 7 7
───────
```

(9)
```
H T U
4 9 1
+ 1 7 9
───────
```

(10)
```
H T U
4 8 8
+ 1 2 2
───────
```

(11)
```
H T U
4 7 3
+ 1 3 9
───────
```

(12)
```
H T U
4 5 7
+ 1 9 9
───────
```

Exercise 12

(1)
```
H T U
4 2 8
+ 6 8 9
───────
```

(2)
```
H T U
5 5 6
+ 5 5 4
───────
```

(3)
```
H T U
6 1 3
+ 6 9 7
───────
```

(4)
```
H T U
5 6 7
+ 4 4 5
───────
```

(5)
```
H T U
5 8 4
+ 4 1 7
───────
```

(6)
```
H T U
5 9 9
+ 5 2 2
───────
```

(7)
```
H T U
6 7 8
+ 3 3 5
───────
```

(8)
```
H T U
6 9 2
+ 3 3 9
───────
```

(9)
```
H T U
6 7 1
+ 9 2 9
───────
```

(10)
```
H T U
6 8 8
+ 6 8 2
───────
```

(11)
```
H T U
7 9 5
+ 7 5 5
───────
```

(12)
```
H T U
7 9 9
+ 9 9 9
───────
```

Exercise 13 Take away tens and units.

(1) T U	(2) T U	(3) T U	(4) T U
2 1	2 2	2 3	2 4
- 1 1	- 1 0	- 1 2	- 1 3

(5) T U	(6) T U	(7) T U	(8) T U
2 5	2 6	2 7	2 8
- 1 4	- 1 3	- 1 4	- 1 4

(9) T U	(10) T U	(11) T U	(12) T U
2 9	3 0	3 3	3 4
- 1 7	- 1 0	- 2 2	- 1 3

(13) T U	(14) T U	(15) T U	(16) T U
3 5	3 6	3 7	3 8
- 1 4	- 2 4	- 2 4	- 2 5

Exercise 14 Subtract tens and units.

(1) T U	(2) T U	(3) T U	(4) T U
3 9	4 2	4 3	4 4
- 2 6	- 1 2	- 1 1	- 1 3

(5) T U	(6) T U	(7) T U	(8) T U
4 5	4 6	4 7	4 8
- 2 4	- 1 3	- 1 4	- 1 5

(9) T U	(10) T U	(11) T U	(12) T U
4 9	5 2	5 3	5 4
- 2 5	- 3 1	- 2 1	- 4 2

(13) T U	(14) T U	(15) T U	(16) T U
5 5	5 6	5 7	5 8
- 1 2	- 1 3	- 4 5	- 2 4

Exercise 16

If you can't take the units, borrow a ten!

(1)
```
T U
2 3
-1 4
___
```
(2)
```
T U
2 4
-1 7
___
```
(3)
```
T U
2 5
-1 7
___
```
(4)
```
T U
2 6
-1 7
___
```

(5)
```
T U
2 7
-1 9
___
```
(6)
```
T U
2 8
-1 9
___
```
(7)
```
T U
2 9
-1 9
___
```
(8)
```
T U
3 0
-2 2
___
```

(9)
```
T U
3 1
-2 6
___
```
(10)
```
T U
3 2
-1 8
___
```
(11)
```
T U
3 3
-2 7
___
```
(12)
```
T U
3 4
-1 5
___
```

(13)
```
T U
3 5
-1 9
___
```
(14)
```
T U
3 6
-2 7
___
```
(15)
```
T U
3 7
-1 8
___
```
(16)
```
T U
3 8
-2 9
___
```

Exercise 15

Find the difference.

(1)
```
T U
6 2
-4 1
___
```
(2)
```
T U
8 5
-5 4
___
```
(3)
```
T U
6 3
-5 1
___
```
(4)
```
T U
6 4
-5 4
___
```

(5)
```
T U
6 5
-2 3
___
```
(6)
```
T U
6 6
-4 5
___
```
(7)
```
T U
6 7
-2 5
___
```
(8)
```
T U
6 8
-5 1
___
```

(9)
```
T U
6 9
-1 3
___
```
(10)
```
T U
7 0
-5 0
___
```
(11)
```
T U
7 1
-2 1
___
```
(12)
```
T U
7 2
-6 1
___
```

(13)
```
T U
7 3
-5 0
___
```
(14)
```
T U
7 4
-5 3
___
```
(15)
```
T U
7 5
-6 1
___
```
(16)
```
T U
7 6
-2 4
___
```

Exercise 17

If you can't take from the units, fetch a ten!

(1)
```
T U
  4 0
- 3 9
-----
```

(2)
```
T U
  4 1
- 2 8
-----
```

(3)
```
T U
  4 2
- 3 5
-----
```

(4)
```
T U
  4 3
- 2 7
-----
```

(5)
```
T U
  4 4
- 2 5
-----
```

(6)
```
T U
  4 5
- 2 6
-----
```

(7)
```
T U
  4 6
- 3 9
-----
```

(8)
```
T U
  4 7
- 2 8
-----
```

(9)
```
T U
  4 8
- 2 9
-----
```

(10)
```
T U
  5 0
- 2 9
-----
```

(11)
```
T U
  5 1
- 2 9
-----
```

(12)
```
T U
  5 2
- 2 9
-----
```

(13)
```
T U
  5 3
- 3 7
-----
```

(14)
```
T U
  5 4
- 2 9
-----
```

(15)
```
T U
  5 5
- 4 6
-----
```

(16)
```
T U
  5 6
- 3 8
-----
```

Exercise 18

Make the top unit larger by adding a ten!

(1)
```
T U
  5 7
- 2 9
-----
```

(2)
```
T U
  5 8
- 2 9
-----
```

(3)
```
T U
  5 8
- 4 9
-----
```

(4)
```
T U
  6 0
- 4 9
-----
```

(5)
```
T U
  6 1
- 5 2
-----
```

(6)
```
T U
  6 2
- 4 3
-----
```

(7)
```
T U
  6 3
- 2 4
-----
```

(8)
```
T U
  6 4
- 1 7
-----
```

(9)
```
T U
  6 5
- 1 6
-----
```

(10)
```
T U
  6 6
- 5 9
-----
```

(11)
```
T U
  6 7
- 4 8
-----
```

(12)
```
T U
  6 8
- 2 9
-----
```

(13)
```
T U
  7 0
- 5 1
-----
```

(14)
```
T U
  7 1
- 4 2
-----
```

(15)
```
T U
  7 2
- 6 9
-----
```

(16)
```
T U
  7 3
- 3 8
-----
```

Exercise 20 — Subtract hundreds, tens and units.

(1)
```
H T U
4 5 6
- 3 3 3
_____
```

(2)
```
H T U
4 2 3
- 2 1 2
_____
```

(3)
```
H T U
4 7 0
- 3 5 0
_____
```

(4)
```
H T U
4 2 3
- 2 1 3
_____
```

(5)
```
H T U
4 5 7
- 2 5 6
_____
```

(6)
```
H T U
4 8 9
- 2 2 5
_____
```

(7)
```
H T U
5 2 4
- 4 1 2
_____
```

(8)
```
H T U
5 5 6
- 3 3 5
_____
```

(9)
```
H T U
5 4 3
- 2 1 2
_____
```

(10)
```
H T U
5 9 8
- 1 7 2
_____
```

(11)
```
H T U
5 7 2
- 2 2 1
_____
```

(12)
```
H T U
5 3 1
- 4 3 1
_____
```

Exercise 19 — Take away hundreds, tens and units.

(1)
```
H T U
2 2 4
- 1 1 3
_____
```

(2)
```
H T U
2 2 9
- 1 1 6
_____
```

(3)
```
H T U
2 2 8
- 1 1 7
_____
```

(4)
```
H T U
2 3 6
- 1 2 4
_____
```

(5)
```
H T U
2 4 8
- 1 3 5
_____
```

(6)
```
H T U
2 6 6
- 1 5 5
_____
```

(7)
```
H T U
3 1 2
- 2 1 0
_____
```

(8)
```
H T U
3 2 6
- 1 1 0
_____
```

(9)
```
H T U
3 2 8
- 2 2 0
_____
```

(10)
```
H T U
3 4 5
- 2 2 2
_____
```

(11)
```
H T U
3 9 7
- 2 7 7
_____
```

(12)
```
H T U
3 6 4
- 2 1 1
_____
```

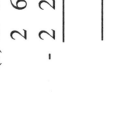

Exercise 21

Find the difference.

(1)
```
H T U
6 4 3
- 4 2 1
-------
```

(2)
```
H T U
6 5 9
- 5 5 5
-------
```

(3)
```
H T U
6 7 2
- 3 5 1
-------
```

(4)
```
H T U
6 8 4
- 5 5 2
-------
```

(5)
```
H T U
6 9 7
- 3 6 6
-------
```

(6)
```
H T U
6 8 5
- 4 4 2
-------
```

(7)
```
H T U
7 7 5
- 5 1 2
-------
```

(8)
```
H T U
7 2 9
- 3 1 7
-------
```

(9)
```
H T U
7 3 8
- 1 1 1
-------
```

(10)
```
H T U
8 7 6
- 2 5 4
-------
```

(11)
```
H T U
9 0 2
- 7 0 1
-------
```

(12)
```
H T U
9 9 9
- 8 6 5
-------
```

Exercise 22

If you can't take the units, borrow a ten

(1)
```
H T U
2 3 5
- 1 1 7
-------
```

(2)
```
H T U
2 1 7
- 1 0 9
-------
```

(3)
```
H T U
2 6 8
- 2 2 9
-------
```

(4)
```
H T U
2 8 8
- 1 6 9
-------
```

(5)
```
H T U
2 7 5
- 1 5 8
-------
```

(6)
```
H T U
2 9 7
- 2 3 9
-------
```

(7)
```
H T U
3 2 5
- 1 1 7
-------
```

(8)
```
H T U
3 4 5
- 2 2 7
-------
```

(9)
```
H T U
3 6 3
- 2 2 9
-------
```

(10)
```
H T U
3 8 5
- 2 6 8
-------
```

(11)
```
H T U
3 7 3
- 2 2 9
-------
```

(12)
```
H T U
3 9 5
- 1 1 9
-------
```

Exercise 23

(1)
```
H T U
4 5 2
- 2 7 1
───────
```

(2)
```
H T U
4 2 2
- 2 9 1
───────
```

(3)
```
H T U
4 5 7
- 1 9 2
───────
```

(4)
```
H T U
4 5 1
- 3 8 0
───────
```

(5)
```
H T U
4 2 3
- 3 8 1
───────
```

(6)
```
H T U
4 9 7
- 1 9 5
───────
```

(7)
```
H T U
5 3 3
- 4 5 2
───────
```

(8)
```
H T U
5 4 6
- 1 8 1
───────
```

(9)
```
H T U
5 7 1
- 1 8 0
───────
```

(10)
```
H T U
5 8 6
- 3 9 4
───────
```

(11)
```
H T U
5 4 2
- 2 6 1
───────
```

(12)
```
H T U
5 7 1
- 1 9 0
───────
```

Exercise 24

(1)
```
H T U
3 3 5
- 2 8 6
───────
```

(2)
```
H T U
2 1 8
- 1 5 9
───────
```

(3)
```
H T U
2 5 6
- 1 7 7
───────
```

(4)
```
H T U
4 8 6
- 3 9 7
───────
```

(5)
```
H T U
5 9 2
- 2 9 9
───────
```

(6)
```
H T U
7 4 1
- 5 8 2
───────
```

(7)
```
H T U
6 6 3
- 3 8 9
───────
```

(8)
```
H T U
8 9 1
- 4 9 2
───────
```

(9)
```
H T U
7 2 4
- 5 5 5
───────
```

(10)
```
H T U
8 8 7
- 2 9 8
───────
```

(11)
```
H T U
9 4 3
- 4 7 5
───────
```

(12)
```
H T U
9 6 1
- 3 9 8
───────
```

Exercise 25 — Tens and units times by 2.

	T U		T U		T U		T U
(1)	1 2 × 2	(2)	1 3 × 2	(3)	1 4 × 2	(4)	1 1 × 2
(5)	2 0 × 2	(6)	2 1 × 2	(7)	2 2 × 2	(8)	2 3 × 2
(9)	2 4 × 2	(10)	3 0 × 2	(11)	3 1 × 2	(12)	3 2 × 2
(13)	3 3 × 2	(14)	3 4 × 2	(15)	4 2 × 2	(16)	4 4 × 2

Exercise 26 — Do you know your 3 times table?

	T U		T U		T U		T U
(1)	1 0 × 3	(2)	1 1 × 3	(3)	1 2 × 3	(4)	1 3 × 3
(5)	2 0 × 3	(6)	2 1 × 3	(7)	2 2 × 3	(8)	2 3 × 3
(9)	3 0 × 3	(10)	3 1 × 3	(11)	3 2 × 3	(12)	3 3 × 3
(13)	0 1 × 3	(14)	0 2 × 3	(15)	0 3 × 3	(16)	4 1 × 3

Exercise 27

	T U		T U		T U		T U
(1)	1 0 x 4	**(2)**	1 0 x 5	**(3)**	1 0 x 6	**(4)**	1 0 x 7
(5)	1 0 x 8	**(6)**	1 0 x 9	**(7)**	1 1 x 4	**(8)**	1 2 x 4
(9)	1 1 x 5	**(10)**	1 1 x 6	**(11)**	1 1 x 7	**(12)**	1 1 x 8
(13)	1 1 x 9	**(14)**	0 1 x 4	**(15)**	0 2 x 4	**(16)**	0 1 x 7

Exercise 28

	T U		T U		T U		T U
(1)	2 5 x 2	**(2)**	2 6 x 2	**(3)**	2 7 x 2	**(4)**	2 8 x 2
(5)	2 9 x 2	**(6)**	3 5 x 2	**(7)**	3 6 x 2	**(8)**	3 7 x 2
(9)	3 8 x 2	**(10)**	3 9 x 2	**(11)**	4 5 x 2	**(12)**	4 6 x 2
(13)	4 7 x 2	**(14)**	4 8 x 2	**(15)**	4 9 x 2	**(16)**	5 5 x 2

(1)
```
T U
2 4
x 3
___
```

(2)
```
T U
2 5
x 3
___
```

(3)
```
T U
2 6
x 3
___
```

(4)
```
T U
2 7
x 3
___
```

(5)
```
T U
2 8
x 3
___
```

(6)
```
T U
2 9
x 3
___
```

(7)
```
T U
3 4
x 3
___
```

(8)
```
T U
3 5
x 3
___
```

(9)
```
T U
3 6
x 3
___
```

(10)
```
T U
3 7
x 3
___
```

(11)
```
T U
3 8
x 3
___
```

(12)
```
T U
3 9
x 3
___
```

(13)
```
T U
4 4
x 3
___
```

(14)
```
T U
4 5
x 3
___
```

(15)
```
T U
4 6
x 3
___
```

(16)
```
T U
4 7
x 3
___
```

(1)
```
T U
1 3
x 4
___
```

(2)
```
T U
1 4
x 4
___
```

(3)
```
T U
1 5
x 4
___
```

(4)
```
T U
1 6
x 4
___
```

(5)
```
T U
1 7
x 4
___
```

(6)
```
T U
1 8
x 4
___
```

(7)
```
T U
1 9
x 4
___
```

(8)
```
T U
2 3
x 4
___
```

(9)
```
T U
1 2
x 5
___
```

(10)
```
T U
1 3
x 5
___
```

(11)
```
T U
1 4
x 5
___
```

(12)
```
T U
1 5
x 5
___
```

(13)
```
T U
1 2
x 6
___
```

(14)
```
T U
1 3
x 6
___
```

(15)
```
T U
1 4
x 7
___
```

(16)
```
T U
1 5
x 7
___
```

Exercise 31

Hundreds, tens and units times 2.

(1) H T U
  1 4 3
  x 2
_____

(2) H T U
  1 3 4
  x 2
_____

(3) H T U
  1 3 0
  x 2
_____

(4) H T U
  2 4 4
  x 2
_____

(5) H T U
  2 4 2
  x 2
_____

(6) H T U
  2 4 3
  x 2
_____

(7) H T U
  3 4 2
  x 2
_____

(8) H T U
  3 3 2
  x 2
_____

(9) H T U
  3 3 3
  x 2
_____

(10) H T U
  4 4 2
  x 2
_____

(11) H T U
  4 2 2
  x 2
_____

(12) H T U
  4 2 4
  x 2
_____

Exercise 32

Hundreds, tens and units times 3

(1) H T U
  1 0 3
  x 3
_____

(2) H T U
  1 2 3
  x 3
_____

(3) H T U
  1 3 0
  x 3
_____

(4) H T U
  2 3 0
  x 3
_____

(5) H T U
  2 1 1
  x 3
_____

(6) H T U
  2 2 3
  x 3
_____

(7) H T U
  3 3 3
  x 3
_____

(8) H T U
  3 2 1
  x 3
_____

(9) H T U
  3 0 0
  x 3
_____

(10) H T U
  3 1 1
  x 3
_____

(11) H T U
  3 2 2
  x 3
_____

(12) H T U
  3 0 3
  x 3
_____

Exercise 33

Do you know all of these tables?

(1) H T U
1 0 1
x 4
_____

(2) H T U
1 2 1
x 4
_____

(3) H T U
1 2 2
x 4
_____

(4) H T U
2 2 0
x 4
_____

(5) H T U
2 1 2
x 4
_____

(6) H T U
1 0 0
x 5
_____

(7) H T U
1 0 1
x 5
_____

(8) H T U
1 0 0
x 6
_____

(9) H T U
1 1 1
x 6
_____

(10) H T U
1 1 1
x 7
_____

(11) H T U
1 0 0
x 8
_____

(12) H T U
1 0 1
x 9
_____

Exercise 34

10 or more in the units? Carry to the tens.

(1) H T U
2 2 5
x 2
_____

(2) H T U
2 3 7
x 2
_____

(3) H T U
2 0 9
x 2
_____

(4) H T U
1 2 6
x 2
_____

(5) H T U
1 3 8
x 2
_____

(6) H T U
2 2 8
x 2
_____

(7) H T U
2 1 4
x 3
_____

(8) H T U
2 2 5
x 3
_____

(9) H T U
2 0 7
x 3
_____

(10) H T U
3 0 8
x 3
_____

(11) H T U
1 2 3
x 4
_____

(12) H T U
1 1 5
x 4
_____

Exercise 35

10 or more in the tens?
Carry to the hundreds.

(1) H T U
  1 5 6
x 2
_____

(2) H T U
  1 7 7
x 2
_____

(3) H T U
  2 9 8
x 2
_____

(4) H T U
  2 4 4
x 3
_____

(5) H T U
  1 5 4
x 3
_____

(6) H T U
  2 6 5
x 3
_____

(7) H T U
  1 3 3
x 4
_____

(8) H T U
  1 2 5
x 4
_____

(9) H T U
  2 2 6
x 4
_____

(10) H T U
  1 3 5
x 5
_____

(11) H T U
  1 2 2
x 5
_____

(12) H T U
  1 3 4
x 5
_____

Exercise 36

10 or more in any column?
Carry to the next.

(1) H T U
  1 2 3
x 6
_____

(2) H T U
  4 2 3
x 6
_____

(3) H T U
  3 3 0
x 6
_____

(4) H T U
  5 3 0
x 7
_____

(5) H T U
  7 1 1
x 7
_____

(6) H T U
  6 2 3
x 7
_____

(7) H T U
  3 3 3
x 8
_____

(8) H T U
  8 2 1
x 8
_____

(9) H T U
  9 0 0
x 8
_____

(10) H T U
  8 1 1
x 9
_____

(11) H T U
  7 2 2
x 9
_____

(12) H T U
  9 0 3
x 9
_____

Exercise 37 — Tens and units shared by 2.

(1) T U	(2) T U	(3) T U	(4) T U
2⟌0 2	2⟌0 4	2⟌0 6	2⟌0 8

(5) T U	(6) T U	(7) T U	(8) T U
2⟌2 0	2⟌4 0	2⟌6 0	2⟌8 0

(9) T U	(10) T U	(11) T U	(12) T U
2⟌2 2	2⟌2 4	2⟌2 6	2⟌2 8

(13) T U	(14) T U	(15) T U	(16) T U
2⟌4 2	2⟌4 4	2⟌4 6	2⟌4 8

(17) T U	(18) T U	(19) T U	(20) T U
2⟌6 2	2⟌6 4	2⟌6 8	2⟌6 6

Exercise 38 — Tens and units divided by 2 or 3

(1) T U	(2) T U	(3) T U	(4) T U
2⟌8 2	2⟌8 4	2⟌8 6	2⟌8 8

(5) T U	(6) T U	(7) T U	(8) T U
3⟌0 3	3⟌0 6	3⟌0 9	3⟌3 0

(9) T U	(10) T U	(11) T U	(12) T U
3⟌3 3	3⟌6 0	3⟌9 0	3⟌3 6

(13) T U	(14) T U	(15) T U	(16) T U
3⟌3 9	3⟌6 3	3⟌6 6	3⟌6 9

(17) T U	(18) T U	(19) T U	(20) T U
3⟌9 3	3⟌9 6	3⟌9 9	4⟌4 0

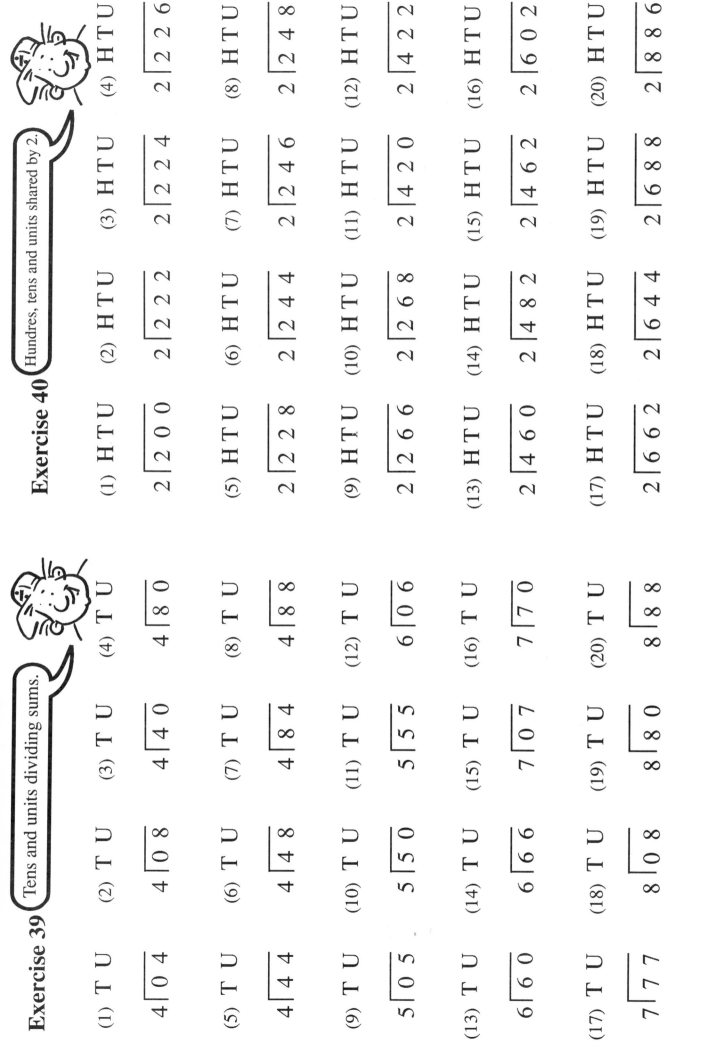

Exercise 39

Tens and units dividing sums.

(1) T U $4\overline{)04}$

(2) T U $4\overline{)08}$

(3) T U $4\overline{)40}$

(4) T U $4\overline{)80}$

(5) T U $4\overline{)44}$

(6) T U $4\overline{)48}$

(7) T U $4\overline{)84}$

(8) T U $4\overline{)88}$

(9) T U $5\overline{)05}$

(10) T U $5\overline{)50}$

(11) T U $5\overline{)55}$

(12) T U $6\overline{)06}$

(13) T U $6\overline{)60}$

(14) T U $6\overline{)66}$

(15) T U $7\overline{)07}$

(16) T U $7\overline{)70}$

(17) T U $7\overline{)77}$

(18) T U $8\overline{)08}$

(19) T U $8\overline{)80}$

(20) T U $8\overline{)88}$

Exercise 40

Hundres, tens and units shared by 2.

(1) H T U $2\overline{)200}$

(2) H T U $2\overline{)222}$

(3) H T U $2\overline{)224}$

(4) H T U $2\overline{)226}$

(5) H T U $2\overline{)228}$

(6) H T U $2\overline{)244}$

(7) H T U $2\overline{)246}$

(8) H T U $2\overline{)248}$

(9) H T U $2\overline{)266}$

(10) H T U $2\overline{)268}$

(11) H T U $2\overline{)420}$

(12) H T U $2\overline{)422}$

(13) H T U $2\overline{)460}$

(14) H T U $2\overline{)482}$

(15) H T U $2\overline{)462}$

(16) H T U $2\overline{)602}$

(17) H T U $2\overline{)662}$

(18) H T U $2\overline{)644}$

(19) H T U $2\overline{)688}$

(20) H T U $2\overline{)886}$

Exercise 41

Hundreds, tens and units divided by 3

(1) H T U
$3\overline{)300}$

(2) H T U
$3\overline{)330}$

(3) H T U
$3\overline{)333}$

(4) H T U
$3\overline{)336}$

(5) H T U
$3\overline{)303}$

(6) H T U
$3\overline{)306}$

(7) H T U
$3\overline{)309}$

(8) H T U
$3\overline{)339}$

(9) H T U
$3\overline{)369}$

(10) H T U
$3\overline{)603}$

(11) H T U
$3\overline{)606}$

(12) H T U
$3\overline{)609}$

(13) H T U
$3\overline{)630}$

(14) H T U
$3\overline{)633}$

(15) H T U
$3\overline{)636}$

(16) H T U
$3\overline{)639}$

(17) H T U
$3\overline{)930}$

(18) H T U
$3\overline{)933}$

(19) H T U
$3\overline{)936}$

(20) H T U
$3\overline{)999}$

Exercise 42

Hundreds, tens and units divided by 4 or 5.

(1) H T U
$4\overline{)400}$

(2) H T U
$4\overline{)404}$

(3) H T U
$4\overline{)444}$

(4) H T U
$4\overline{)044}$

(5) H T U
$4\overline{)004}$

(6) H T U
$4\overline{)440}$

(7) H T U
$4\overline{)408}$

(8) H T U
$4\overline{)480}$

(9) H T U
$4\overline{)804}$

(10) H T U
$4\overline{)840}$

(11) H T U
$4\overline{)844}$

(12) H T U
$4\overline{)848}$

(13) H T U
$4\overline{)488}$

(14) H T U
$4\overline{)808}$

(15) H T U
$4\overline{)880}$

(16) H T U
$4\overline{)808}$

(17) H T U
$4\overline{)088}$

(18) H T U
$5\overline{)505}$

(19) H T U
$5\overline{)550}$

(20) H T U
$5\overline{)555}$

Exercise 43

Tens and units with a remainder

(1) T U	(2) T U	(3) T U	(4) T U
2⟌2 3	2⟌2 5	2⟌2 7	2⟌2 9

(5) T U	(6) T U	(7) T U	(8) T U
2⟌4 3	2⟌4 5	2⟌4 7	2⟌4 9

(9) T U	(10) T U	(11) T U	(12) T U
2⟌6 3	2⟌6 5	2⟌6 7	2⟌6 9

(13) T U	(14) T U	(15) T U	(16) T U
2⟌8 3	2⟌8 5	2⟌8 7	2⟌8 9

(17) T U	(18) T U	(19) T U	(20) T U
2⟌2 1	2⟌4 1	2⟌6 1	2⟌8 1

Exercise 44

Do all these sums have a remainder?

(1) T U	(2) T U	(3) T U	(4) T U
3⟌3 4	3⟌3 7	3⟌3 5	3⟌3 8

(5) T U	(6) T U	(7) T U	(8) T U
3⟌6 4	3⟌6 7	3⟌6 5	3⟌6 8

(9) T U	(10) T U	(11) T U	(12) T U
3⟌9 4	3⟌9 7	3⟌9 5	3⟌9 8

(13) T U	(14) T U	(15) T U	(16) T U
3⟌3 1	3⟌3 2	3⟌6 1	3⟌6 2

(17) T U	(18) T U	(19) T U	(20) T U
3⟌9 1	3⟌9 2	4⟌4 5	4⟌4 6

Exercise 45

Dividing tens and units with a remainder.

(1) T U $4\overline{)45}$ (2) T U $4\overline{)46}$ (3) T U $4\overline{)47}$ (4) T U $4\overline{)49}$

(5) T U $4\overline{)85}$ (6) T U $4\overline{)86}$ (7) T U $4\overline{)87}$ (8) T U $4\overline{)89}$

(9) T U $4\overline{)41}$ (10) T U $4\overline{)42}$ (11) T U $4\overline{)43}$ (12) T U $4\overline{)81}$

(13) T U $4\overline{)82}$ (14) T U $4\overline{)83}$ (15) T U $5\overline{)56}$ (16) T U $5\overline{)57}$

(17) T U $5\overline{)58}$ (18) T U $5\overline{)59}$ (19) T U $5\overline{)51}$ (20) T U $5\overline{)52}$

Exercise 46

What do you notice about these remainders?

(1) H T U $2\overline{)223}$ (2) H T U $2\overline{)245}$ (3) H T U $2\overline{)267}$ (4) H T U $2\overline{)289}$

(5) H T U $2\overline{)243}$ (6) H T U $2\overline{)265}$ (7) H T U $2\overline{)287}$ (8) H T U $2\overline{)229}$

(9) H T U $2\overline{)263}$ (10) H T U $2\overline{)285}$ (11) H T U $2\overline{)227}$ (12) H T U $2\overline{)249}$

(13) H T U $2\overline{)283}$ (14) H T U $2\overline{)225}$ (15) H T U $2\overline{)247}$ (16) H T U $2\overline{)269}$

(17) H T U $2\overline{)221}$ (18) H T U $2\overline{)241}$ (19) H T U $2\overline{)681}$ (20) H T U $2\overline{)861}$

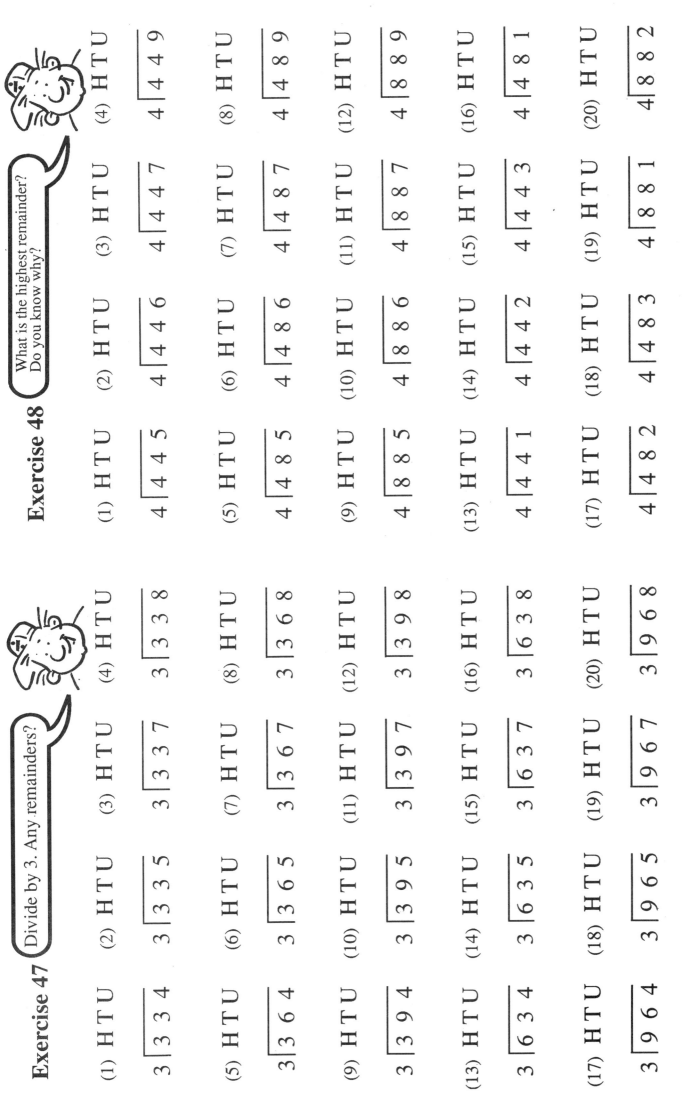

Exercise 47

Divide by 3. Any remainders?

(1) HTU 3|334   (2) HTU 3|335   (3) HTU 3|337   (4) HTU 3|338

(5) HTU 3|364   (6) HTU 3|365   (7) HTU 3|367   (8) HTU 3|368

(9) HTU 3|394   (10) HTU 3|395   (11) HTU 3|397   (12) HTU 3|398

(13) HTU 3|634   (14) HTU 3|635   (15) HTU 3|637   (16) HTU 3|638

(17) HTU 3|964   (18) HTU 3|965   (19) HTU 3|967   (20) HTU 3|968

Exercise 48

What is the highest remainder? Do you know why?

(1) HTU 4|445   (2) HTU 4|446   (3) HTU 4|447   (4) HTU 4|449

(5) HTU 4|485   (6) HTU 4|486   (7) HTU 4|487   (8) HTU 4|489

(9) HTU 4|885   (10) HTU 4|886   (11) HTU 4|887   (12) HTU 4|889

(13) HTU 4|441   (14) HTU 4|442   (15) HTU 4|443   (16) HTU 4|481

(17) HTU 4|482   (18) HTU 4|483   (19) HTU 4|881   (20) HTU 4|882

Exercise 49

Remainder in the middle of a sum? Carry it to the next column.

(1) T U	(2) T U	(3) T U	(4) T U
2)36	2)54	2)72	2)98

(5) T U	(6) T U	(7) T U	(8) T U
3)42	3)54	3)75	3)87

(9) T U	(10) T U	(11) T U	(12) T U
4)52	4)64	4)72	4)12

(13) T U	(14) T U	(15) T U	(16) T U
5)65	5)75	5)80	5)10

(17) T U	(18) T U	(19) T U	(20) T U
6)78	6)84	6)96	6)18

Exercise 50

Always start divide sums from the left.

(1) T U	(2) T U	(3) T U	(4) T U
3)81	3)78	3)54	3)48

(5) T U	(6) T U	(7) T U	(8) T U
4)24	4)72	4)68	4)56

(9) T U	(10) T U	(11) T U	(12) T U
5)10	5)85	5)70	5)65

(13) T U	(14) T U	(15) T U	(16) T U
6)72	6)18	6)84	6)96

(17) T U	(18) T U	(19) T U	(20) T U
7)84	7)91	7)14	7)35

Exercise 52

(1) H T U
$2\overline{)216}$

(2) H T U
$2\overline{)218}$

(3) H T U
$2\overline{)232}$

(4) H T U
$2\overline{)252}$

(5) H T U
$2\overline{)254}$

(6) H T U
$2\overline{)272}$

(7) H T U
$2\overline{)276}$

(8) H T U
$2\overline{)278}$

(9) H T U
$2\overline{)184}$

(10) H T U
$2\overline{)146}$

(11) H T U
$2\overline{)322}$

(12) H T U
$2\overline{)344}$

(13) H T U
$2\overline{)524}$

(14) H T U
$2\overline{)586}$

(15) H T U
$2\overline{)748}$

(16) H T U
$2\overline{)782}$

(17) H T U
$2\overline{)532}$

(18) H T U
$2\overline{)332}$

(19) H T U
$2\overline{)738}$

(20) H T U
$2\overline{)552}$

Exercise 51

(1) T U
$5\overline{)25}$

(2) T U
$5\overline{)35}$

(3) T U
$5\overline{)40}$

(4) T U
$5\overline{)60}$

(5) T U
$6\overline{)24}$

(6) T U
$6\overline{)30}$

(7) T U
$6\overline{)42}$

(8) T U
$6\overline{)54}$

(9) T U
$7\overline{)42}$

(10) T U
$7\overline{)56}$

(11) T U
$7\overline{)63}$

(12) T U
$7\overline{)84}$

(13) T U
$8\overline{)96}$

(14) T U
$8\overline{)32}$

(15) T U
$8\overline{)40}$

(16) T U
$8\overline{)56}$

(17) T U
$9\overline{)18}$

(18) T U
$9\overline{)27}$

(19) T U
$9\overline{)36}$

(20) T U
$9\overline{)45}$

Exercise 53

I hope you know your 3 times table well for these!

(1) HTU $3\overline{)342}$ (2) HTU $3\overline{)354}$ (3) HTU $3\overline{)378}$ (4) HTU $3\overline{)675}$

(5) HTU $3\overline{)621}$ (6) HTU $3\overline{)615}$ (7) HTU $3\overline{)948}$ (8) HTU $3\overline{)987}$

(9) HTU $3\overline{)213}$ (10) HTU $3\overline{)423}$ (11) HTU $3\overline{)573}$ (12) HTU $3\overline{)786}$

(13) HTU $3\overline{)846}$ (14) HTU $3\overline{)186}$ (15) HTU $3\overline{)219}$ (16) HTU $3\overline{)279}$

(17) HTU $3\overline{)528}$ (18) HTU $3\overline{)738}$ (19) HTU $3\overline{)825}$ (20) HTU $3\overline{)138}$

Exercise 54

How well do you know your 4 times table?

(1) HTU $4\overline{)328}$ (2) HTU $4\overline{)244}$ (3) HTU $4\overline{)168}$ (4) HTU $4\overline{)468}$

(5) HTU $4\overline{)520}$ (6) HTU $4\overline{)536}$ (7) HTU $4\overline{)540}$ (8) HTU $4\overline{)552}$

(9) HTU $4\overline{)684}$ (10) HTU $4\overline{)656}$ (11) HTU $4\overline{)692}$ (12) HTU $4\overline{)636}$

(13) HTU $4\overline{)728}$ (14) HTU $4\overline{)748}$ (15) HTU $4\overline{)756}$ (16) HTU $4\overline{)784}$

(17) HTU $4\overline{)988}$ (18) HTU $4\overline{)944}$ (19) HTU $4\overline{)992}$ (20) HTU $4\overline{)980}$

Exercise 55

(Dividing, carrying and remainders!)

(1) T U

(2) T U

$2\overline{)33}$

(3) T U

$2\overline{)37}$

(4) T U

$2\overline{)39}$

(5) T U

(6) T U

$2\overline{)55}$

(7) T U

$2\overline{)71}$

(8) T U

$2\overline{)75}$

(9) T U

(10) T U

$2\overline{)93}$

(11) T U

$2\overline{)97}$

(12) T U

$3\overline{)22}$

(13) T U

(14) T U

$3\overline{)41}$

(15) T U

$3\overline{)47}$

(16) T U

$3\overline{)48}$

(17) T U

(18) T U

$3\overline{)53}$

(19) T U

$3\overline{)74}$

(20) T U

$3\overline{)88}$

$2\overline{)91}$

$3\overline{)28}$

$3\overline{)52}$

Exercise 56

Hope you know your 4 times and 5 times tables!

(1) T U

(2) T U

$4\overline{)75}$

(3) T U

$4\overline{)83}$

(4) T U

$4\overline{)93}$

(5) T U

(6) T U

$4\overline{)61}$

(7) T U

$4\overline{)73}$

(8) T U

$4\overline{)33}$

(9) T U

(10) T U

$4\overline{)97}$

(11) T U

$5\overline{)24}$

(12) T U

$5\overline{)68}$

(13) T U

(14) T U

$5\overline{)84}$

(15) T U

$5\overline{)89}$

(16) T U

$5\overline{)97}$

(17) T U

(18) T U

$5\overline{)47}$

(19) T U

$5\overline{)52}$

(20) T U

$5\overline{)63}$

$4\overline{)63}$

$4\overline{)54}$

$4\overline{)89}$

$5\overline{)73}$

$5\overline{)31}$

Exercise 58

H.T.U., dividing, carrying and remainders – what a lot!

(1) H T U 2|179
(2) H T U 2|531
(3) H T U 2|719
(4) H T U 2|355
(5) H T U 2|527
(6) H T U 2|731
(7) H T U 2|893
(8) H T U 2|747
(9) H T U 3|551
(10) H T U 3|742
(11) H T U 3|871
(12) H T U 3|972
(13) H T U 3|142
(14) H T U 3|227
(15) H T U 3|893
(16) H T U 3|746
(17) H T U 4|725
(18) H T U 4|339
(19) H T U 4|529
(20) H T U 4|771

Exercise 57

And now use all the other tables.

(1) T U 6|73
(2) T U 6|75
(3) T U 6|81
(4) T U 6|83
(5) T U 6|87
(6) T U 6|91
(7) T U 7|82
(8) T U 7|85
(9) T U 7|89
(10) T U 7|93
(11) T U 7|62
(12) T U 7|25
(13) T U 8|89
(14) T U 8|92
(15) T U 8|27
(16) T U 8|53
(17) T U 9|92
(18) T U 9|97
(19) T U 9|38
(20) T U 9|71

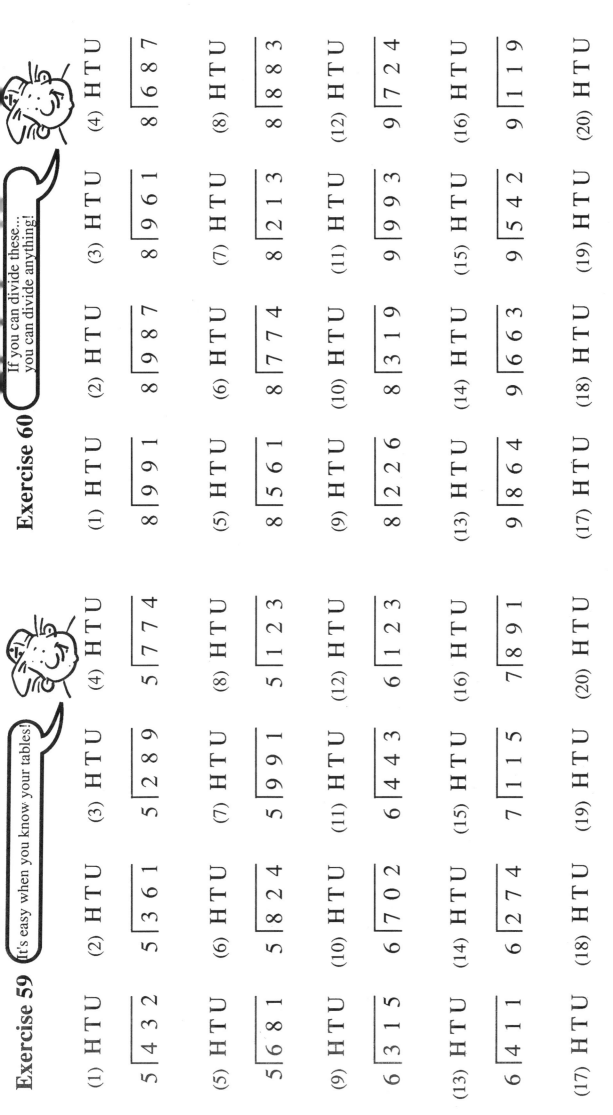

Exercise 60

If you can divide these...
you can divide anything!

(1) HTU 8)991 (2) HTU 8)987 (3) HTU 8)961 (4) HTU 8)687

(5) HTU 8)561 (6) HTU 8)774 (7) HTU 8)213 (8) HTU 8)883

(9) HTU 8)226 (10) HTU 8)319 (11) HTU 9)993 (12) HTU 9)724

(13) HTU 9)864 (14) HTU 9)663 (15) HTU 9)542 (16) HTU 9)119

(17) HTU 9)229 (18) HTU 9)770 (19) HTU 9)236 (20) HTU 9)740

Exercise 59

It's easy when you know your tables!

(1) HTU 5)432 (2) HTU 5)361 (3) HTU 5)289 (4) HTU 5)774

(5) HTU 5)681 (6) HTU 5)824 (7) HTU 5)991 (8) HTU 5)123

(9) HTU 6)315 (10) HTU 6)702 (11) HTU 6)443 (12) HTU 6)123

(13) HTU 6)411 (14) HTU 6)274 (15) HTU 7)115 (16) HTU 7)891

(17) HTU 7)734 (18) HTU 7)964 (19) HTU 7)853 (20) HTU 7)422

Exercise 61 Revision

(1)
```
  2 3 4
+ 7 5 8
  1 6 9
```

(2)
```
  3 4 7
+ 1 2 2
  7 5 3
```

(3)
```
  7 4 2
+ 8 6 6
  1 0 2
```

(4)
```
  9 9 8
+ 4 3 3
  1 2 5
```

(5)
```
  7 4 2
- 5 8 8
```

(6)
```
  9 3 4
- 3 8 6
```

(7)
```
  4 2 5
-   8 9
```

(8)
```
  7 3 3
- 6 5 2
```

(9)
```
  4 4 2
x   2
```

(10)
```
  6 5 4
x   3
```

(11)
```
  7 2 2
x   4
```

(12)
```
  3 6 9
x   5
```

(13) 2 | 6 4 4

(14) 3 | 9 6 8

(15) 4 | 4 7 9

(16) 5 | 8 3 7

(17) Add together 17, 57 and 44.

(18) What is 566 take away 345?

(19) What is 266 times 5?

(20) Divide 636 by 6.

(21) Add together 75, 85 and 95.

(22) 709 take away 388.

(23) What is 764 times 7?

(24) Divide 192 by 4.

(25) 64 add 604 add 6004.

(26) 744 minus 477.

(27) 2844 times 5.

(28) What is 3632 divided by 4?

(29) Find the total of 466, 399 and 3865.

(30) Find the difference between 633 and 276.

(31) Multiply 36 by 6.

(32) Share 2709 by 7.

(33) What is the sum of 255, 4436 and 5009?

(34) Subtract 314 from 3014.

(35) Multiply 4546 by 5.

(36) Divide 2768 by 8.

(37) Find the total of 455, 2882 and 3666.

(38) Find the difference between 4462 and 338.

(39) Multiply 6539 by 9.

(40) Divide 4545 by 5.

Exercise 62 Revision

(1)
```
  2 2 4
+ 3 5 1
  1 1 1
```

(2)
```
  7 2 3
+ 6 2 7
  3 9 9
```

(3)
```
  2 6 4
+ 7 2 1
  3 9 8
```

(4)
```
  6 6 6
+ 5 2 4
  7 3 9
```

(5)
```
  2 4 3
- 1 1 2
```

(6)
```
  7 8 5
- 3 6 9
```

(7)
```
  7 1 1
- 2 9 6
```

(8)
```
  3 7 2
- 1 8 7
```

(9)
```
  1 2 3
   x 2
```

(10)
```
  3 4 5
   x 3
```

(11)
```
  8 4 2
   x 4
```

(12)
```
  5 2 9
   x 5
```

(13) 2 | 2 8 6

(14) 3 | 1 2 9

(15) 4 | 6 2 1

(16) 5 | 9 9 0

(17) Add together 18, 56 and 35.

(18) What is 356 take away 222?

(19) What is 256 times 4?

(20) Divide 785 by 5.

(21) Add together 56, 89 and 47.

(22) 897 take away 347.

(23) What is 456 times 8?

(24) Divide 452 by 4.

(25) 75 add 705 add 7005.

(26) 366 minus 298.

(27) 4522 times 6.

(28) What is 4565 divided by 5?

(29) Find the total of 23, 230 and 5688.

(30) Find the difference between 577 and 348.

(31) Multiply 42 by 7.

(32) Share 5608 by 4.

(33) What is the sum of 23, 563 and 2345?

(34) Subtract 214 from 2014.

(35) Multiply 5438 by 6.

(36) Divide 5432 by 7.

(37) Find the total of 344, 5673 and 234.

(38) Find the difference between 4461 and 291.

(39) Multiply 5688 by 8.

(40) Divide 5679 by 9.

Exercise 63 Revision

(1)
```
  5 2 1
+ 3 6 5
  1 4 2
```

(2)
```
  4 7 9
+ 1 1 1
  4 2 3
```

(3)
```
  4 2 3
+ 6 8 8
  1 4 5
```

(4)
```
  6 4 4
+ 2 2 2
  3 6 1
```

(5)
```
  6 2 3
- 1 2 2
```

(6)
```
  7 4 6
- 5 2 7
```

(7)
```
  7 3 4
- 5 8 9
```

(8)
```
  4 0 0
- 3 1 9
```

(9)
```
  2 4 2
x   2
```

(10)
```
  3 6 5
x   4
```

(11)
```
  7 2 3
x   6
```

(12)
```
  8 0 1
x   7
```

(13) 2 | 6 6 4

(14) 3 | 7 2 3

(15) 5 | 7 2 0

(16) 6 | 5 8 9

---

(17) Add together 23, 456 and 705.

(18) What is 94 take away 66?

(19) Multiply 46 by 6.

(20) Divide 840 by 4.

(21) What is the sum of 567 and 23?

(22) Find the difference between 96 and 84.

(23) What is 659 times 6?

(24) Divide 70 by 5.

(25) Add 27, 270, 2700 and 2007.

(26) How much is 156 less than 275?

(27) 5672 times 7.

(28) 4530 divided by 6?

(29) How much is 245 add 320 add 500?

(30) What is 375 less 205?

(31) Multiply 75 by 4.

(32) 652 divided by 6?

(33) What is the total of 5500 , 3875 and 6200 ?

(34) 7600 take away 5?

(35) 8 times 564?

(36) Divide 4000 by 8.

(37) 6 add 66 add 666 add 6666?

(38) Find the difference between 1075 and 875.

(39) 578 x 6?

(40) 750 divided by 5?

Exercise 64 Revision

(1)
```
  2 2 2
+ 1 5 4
  3 1 5
———————
```

(2)
```
  7 4 1
+ 3 8 9
  4 2 1
———————
```

(3)
```
  7 3 4
+ 2 1 7
  8 2 1
———————
```

(4)
```
  7 5 9
+ 6 3 3
  2 2 4
———————
```

(5)
```
  2 4 6
- 1 2 5
———————
```

(6)
```
  3 7 4
- 1 9 3
———————
```

(7)
```
  2 4 6
- 1 5 7
———————
```

(8)
```
  1 0 0
-   8 7
———————
```

(9)
```
  2 2 2
×   2
———————
```

(10)
```
  2 3 4
×   3
———————
```

(11)
```
  6 2 5
×   4
———————
```

(12)
```
  7 2 9
×   5
———————
```

(13)
$$2\,\overline{)8\ 6\ 4}$$

(14)
$$3\,\overline{)3\ 0\ 9}$$

(15)
$$4\,\overline{)2\ 0\ 8}$$

(16)
$$5\,\overline{)7\ 4\ 5}$$

(17) Add 345, 536 and 678.

(18) What is 1089 take away 456?

(19) What is 456 times 6?

(20) Divide 100 by 5.

(21) Add together 1006, 345 and 2345.

(22) 788 take away 500.

(23) What is 76 times 9?

(24) Divide 677 by 8.

(25) 24 add 240 add 2400.

(26) 7865 minus 67.

(27) 899 times 5.

(28) What is 1684 divided by 4?

(29) Find the total of 178, 185 and 75.

(30) Find the difference between 1000 and 780.

(31) 550 times 6.

(32) Share 560 by 4.

(33) What is the sum of 34, 45 and 67?

(34) Subtract 899 from 1000.

(35) Multiply 250 by 4.

(36) Divide 679 by 7.

(37) Find the total of 7896, 4568 and 3489.

(38) Find the difference between 5689 and 4569.

(39) Multiply 4009 by 6.

(40) Divide 891 by 9.

Exercise 65 Revision

(1)
```
  2 3 5
+ 7 6 6
  1 5 9
```

(2)
```
  3 4 7
+ 1 3 5
  7 2 5
```

(3)
```
  7 7 2
+ 8 0 6
  1 3 9
```

(4)
```
  9 2 3
+ 4 7 1
  1 6 5
```

(5)
```
  8 2 1
- 3 6 5
```

(6)
```
  2 4 7
- 1 0 6
```

(7)
```
  3 0 0
- 2 8 9
```

(8)
```
  7 2 3
- 4 1 5
```

(9)
```
  2 2 5
  x 3
```

(10)
```
  6 3 1
  x 4
```

(11)
```
  7 2 0
  x 6
```

(12)
```
  3 5 9
  x 7
```

(13) 2 | 8 4 2

(14) 3 | 6 9 4

(15) 4 | 3 2 1

(16) 6 | 7 8 9

(17) Add together 67, 670 and 6700.

(18) What is 567 take away 359?

(19) What is 563 times 6?

(20) Divide 497 by 7.

(21) Add together 43, 145 and 56.

(22) 893 take away 781.

(23) What is 445 times 4?

(24) Divide 343 by 7.

(25) 78 add 788 add 78888.

(26) 897 minus 432.

(27) 5066 times 6.

(28) What is 8885 divided by 5?

(29) Find the total of 4532, 8778 and 4322.

(30) Find the difference between 805 and 405.

(31) Multiply 48 by 7.

(32) Share 560 by 8.

(33) What is the sum of 566, 6000 and 7800?

(34) Subtract 406 from 1640.

(35) Multiply 2380 by 4.

(36) Divide 5784 by 8.

(37) Find the total of 453, 4556 and 27.

(38) Find the difference between 4556 and 36.

(39) Multiply 4583 by 9.

(40) Divide 5688 by 9.

Exercise 66 Revision

(1)
```
  2 7 1
+ 1 1 1
  3 0 5
```

(2)
```
  7 2 9
+ 2 2 4
  8 1 1
```

(3)
```
  3 2 9
+ 7 2 0
  8 0 0
```

(4)
```
  4 2 7
+ 8 3 1
  7 7 7
```

(5)
```
  7 2 1
- 1 6 5
```

(6)
```
  8 3 0
- 2 8 8
```

(7)
```
  9 1 5
- 7 2 4
```

(8)
```
  7 2 5
- 6 6 6
```

(9)
```
  2 2 2
  x   3
```

(10)
```
  3 4 1
  x   5
```

(11)
```
  5 7 0
  x   6
```

(12)
```
  3 9 5
  x   8
```

(13) 2 | 8 6 3

(14) 4 | 7 3 2

(15) 5 | 8 0 5

(16) 6 | 3 7 2

(17) Add together 678, 965 and 5.

(18) What is 789 take away 320?

(19) What is 567 times 7?

(20) Divide 600 by 5.

(21) Add together 5, 65 and 655.

(22) 896 take away 45.

(23) What is 943 times 7?

(24) Divide 568 by 4.

(25) 56 add 506 add 5006.

(26) 899 minus 400.

(27) 2345 times 6.

(28) What is 7868 divided by 7?

(29) Find the total of 456, 7839 and 72.

(30) Find the difference between 789 and 599.

(31) Multiply 49 by 7.

(32) Share 5800 by 8.

(33) What is the sum of 34, 567 and 7896?

(34) Subtract 304 from 4007.

(35) Multiply 5448 by 8.

(36) Divide 5784 by 6.

(37) Find the total of 23, 2300 and 230.

(38) Find the difference between 4587 and 4593.

(39) Multiply 5688 by 8.

(40) Divide 789635 by 5.

Exercise 67 Revision

(1)
```
  1 2 3
+ 5 6 1
  1 4 1
───────
```

(2)
```
  5 1 4
+ 3 7 2
  7 2 3
───────
```

(3)
```
  9 2 5
+ 1 2 5
  8 0 9
───────
```

(4)
```
  1 4 7
+ 2 5 8
  3 6 9
───────
```

(5)
```
  6 4 3
- 3 4 1
───────
```

(6)
```
  8 0 3
- 7 2 4
───────
```

(7)
```
  4 2 4
- 3 7 9
───────
```

(8)
```
  6 4 4
- 4 9 7
───────
```

(9)
```
  2 7 5
    x 4
───────
```

(10)
```
  2 4 7
    x 5
───────
```

(11)
```
  7 5 0
    x 6
───────
```

(12)
```
  3 7 0
    x 6
───────
```

(13) 5 | 6 1 5

(14) 3 | 1 2 3

(15) 6 | 5 5 7

(16) 8 | 4 0 8

(17) Add together 543, 376 and 17.

(18) What is 675 take away 352?

(19) What is 247 times 7?

(20) Divide 634 by 2.

(21) Add together 9, 75 and 579

(22) 953 take away 46.

(23) What is 352 times 5?

(24) Divide 720 by 5.

(25) 14 add 401 add 1041.

(26) 675 minus 340.

(27) 3456 times 6.

(28) What is 246914 divided by 2?

(29) Find the total of 17, 24639 and 95.

(30) Find the difference between 875 and 611.

(31) Multiply 67 by 9.

(32) Share 2100 by 6.

(33) What is the sum of 1253, 330 and 49?

(34) Subtract 13 from 5012.

(35) Multiply 6172839455 by 2.

(36) Divide 916 by 7.

(37) Find the total of 91, 9909 and 19.

(38) Find the difference between 76854 and 76829.

(39) Multiply 4736 by 6.

(40) Divide 2463 by 4.

Exercise 68 Revision

(1)
```
   6 5 4
 + 1 0 9
   2 3 0
 ———————
```

(2)
```
   1 8 4
 + 1 9 3
   2 0 6
 ———————
```

(3)
```
   5 1 6
 + 3 7 1
   2 4 1
 ———————
```

(4)
```
   3 4 1
 + 9 2 9
   9 1 9
 ———————
```

(5)
```
   5 9 1
 - 4 9 9
 ———————
```

(6)
```
   7 2 0
 - 1 5 1
 ———————
```

(7)
```
   6 0 6
 - 1 4 8
 ———————
```

(8)
```
   8 9 0
 - 5 3 9
 ———————
```

(9)
```
   1 2 5
     x 4
 ———————
```

(10)
```
   6 3 2
     x 4
 ———————
```

(11)
```
   7 1 5
     x 8
 ———————
```

(12)
```
   6 3 9
     x 9
 ———————
```

(13) $7 \overline{| 5 7 6}$

(14) $6 \overline{| 4 9 9}$

(15) $5 \overline{| 8 8 8}$

(16) $2 \overline{| 1 1 1}$

(17) Add together 24, 543 and 895.

(18) What is 758 take away 120?

(19) What is 185 times 3?

(20) Divide 741 by 3.

(21) Add together 134, 431 and 222.

(22) 578 take away 420.

(23) What is 536 times 7?

(24) Divide 975 by 5.

(25) 34 add 999 add 7.

(26) 906 minus 356.

(27) 428 times 4.

(28) What is 74070 divided by 6?

(29) Find the total of 406, 54 and 800.

(30) Find the difference between 642 and 431.

(31) Multiply 839 by 4.

(32) Share 647 by 2.

(33) What is the sum of 56, 457 and 257?

(34) Subtract 257 from 752.

(35) Multiply 342 by 9.

(36) Divide 1476 by 6.

(37) Find the total of 74, 345 and 368.

(38) Find the difference between 456 and 231.

(39) Multiply 651 by 3.

(40) Divide 96765 by 3.

Exercise 69 Revision

(1)
```
    4 5 4
  + 1 8 9
    2 2 0
  _____
```

(2)
```
    5 8 2
  + 4 9 5
    3 7 6
  _____
```

(3)
```
    7 3 6
  + 6 1 1
    4 6 1
  _____
```

(4)
```
    6 3 1
  + 6 8 9
    2 1 3
  _____
```

(5)
```
    4 9 1
  - 3 2 9
  _____
```

(6)
```
    6 1 0
  - 4 5 1
  _____
```

(7)
```
    8 0 6
  - 5 9 8
  _____
```

(8)
```
    7 0 0
  - 6 8 9
  _____
```

(9)
```
    8 2 5
    x   5
  _____
```

(10)
```
    8 3 2
    x   6
  _____
```

(11)
```
    3 7 5
    x   7
  _____
```

(12)
```
    1 5 9
    x   9
  _____
```

(13) 3 | 6 6 7

(14) 5 | 8 9 9

(15) 6 | 4 3 8

(16) 8 | 1 7 6

(17) Add together 34, 843 and 255.

(18) What is 828 take away 178?

(19) What is 385 times 7?

(20) Divide 871 by 4.

(21) Add together 234, 431 and 289.

(22) 928 take away 530.

(23) What is 286 times 8?

(24) Divide 3345 by 5.

(25) 58 add 649 add 9.

(26) 924 minus 776.

(27) 328 times 6.

(28) What is 6474 divided by 6?

(29) Find the total of 217, 54 and 564.

(30) Find the difference between 663 and 189.

(31) Multiply 935 by 4.

(32) Share 9874 by 2.

(33) What is the sum of 43, 466 and 357?

(34) Subtract 377 from 882.

(35) Multiply 442 by 8.

(36) Divide 1296 by 6.

(37) Find the total of 94, 785 and 496.

(38) Find the difference between 356 and 289.

(39) Multiply 984 by 4.

(40) Divide 897420 by 4.

Exercise 70 Revision

(1)
```
   6 3 7
 + 1 3 0
   2 3 2
 _____
```

(2)
```
   5 5 4
 + 7 4 9
   3 1 4
 _____
```

(3)
```
   4 3 7
 + 1 9 1
   9 0 2
 _____
```

(4)
```
   6 5 9
 + 4 6 2
   8 8 6
 _____
```

(5)
```
   4 0 0
 - 2 9 4
 _____
```

(6)
```
   6 9 4
 - 2 0 9
 _____
```

(7)
```
   8 1 1
 - 1 8 8
 _____
```

(8)
```
   6 6 5
 - 2 3 9
 _____
```

(9)
```
   3 1 9
   x   5
 _____
```

(10)
```
   5 5 8
   x   7
 _____
```

(11)
```
   8 8 9
   x   3
 _____
```

(12)
```
   4 6 1
   x   9
 _____
```

(13) 6 | 3 1 2

(14) 2 | 5 0 5

(15) 8 | 6 1 5

(16) 4 | 1 5 1

---

(17) Add together 254, 898 and 140.

(18) What is 990 take away 41?

(19) What is 758 times 2?

(20) Divide 679 by 4.

(21) Add together 78, 246 and 991.

(22) 748 take away 487.

(23) What is 739 times 9?

(24) Divide 999 by 7.

(25) 71 add 142 add 284.

(26) 974 minus 160.

(27) 930 times 3.

(28) What is 61725 divided by 5?

(29) Find the total of 94, 914 and 975.

(30) Find the difference between 99 and 1008.

(31) Multiply 578 by 7.

(32) Share 359 by 3.

(33) What is the sum of 896, 25 and 429?

(34) Subtract 275 from 997.

(35) Multiply 467 by 0.

(36) Divide 1029 by 6.

(37) Find the total of 4000, 647 and 785.

(38) Find the difference between 8934 and 1006.

(39) Multiply 6078 by 2.

(40) Divide 3528 by 8.

Exercise 72

(1) 2 1 5
x 4 2
_____

(2) 2 2 7
x 4 5
_____

(3) 2 3 9
x 4 7
_____

(4) 1 2 6
x 4 9
_____

(5) 1 3 8
x 5 2
_____

(6) 2 6 8
x 5 5
_____

(7) 2 8 4
x 6 3
_____

(8) 2 2 5
x 6 1
_____

(9) 2 7 7
x 6 3
_____

(10) 3 1 8
x 6 7
_____

(11) 1 4 3
x 6 8
_____

(12) 1 8 5
x 6 9
_____

Exercise 71

(1) 1 6 1
x 2 4
_____

(2) 1 7 1
x 2 5
_____

(3) 1 2 2
x 2 6
_____

(4) 2 3 0
x 2 7
_____

(5) 2 1 2
x 2 8
_____

(6) 1 5 0
x 2 9
_____

(7) 1 6 1
x 3 0
_____

(8) 1 7 0
x 3 2
_____

(9) 1 8 1
x 3 6
_____

(10) 1 8 2
x 3 7
_____

(11) 1 3 4
x 3 8
_____

(12) 1 2 7
x 4 1
_____

Exercise 74

(1) 6 1 5
 × 5 2
 ———

(2) 7 2 7
 × 5 5
 ———

(3) 8 3 9
 × 5 7
 ———

(4) 9 2 6
 × 5 9
 ———

(5) 2 3 8
 × 6 2
 ———

(6) 3 6 8
 × 6 5
 ———

(7) 4 8 4
 × 6 3
 ———

(8) 5 2 5
 × 7 1
 ———

(9) 6 7 7
 × 7 3
 ———

(10) 7 1 8
 × 7 7
 ———

(11) 8 4 3
 × 7 8
 ———

(12) 9 8 5
 × 7 9
 ———

Exercise 73

(1) 2 6 1
 × 3 4
 ———

(2) 3 7 1
 × 3 5
 ———

(3) 4 2 2
 × 3 6
 ———

(4) 5 3 0
 × 3 7
 ———

(5) 6 1 2
 × 3 8
 ———

(6) 7 5 0
 × 3 9
 ———

(7) 8 6 1
 × 4 0
 ———

(8) 9 7 0
 × 4 2
 ———

(9) 2 8 1
 × 4 6
 ———

(10) 3 8 2
 × 4 7
 ———

(11) 4 3 4
 × 4 8
 ———

(12) 5 2 7
 × 5 1
 ———

Exercise 76

(1) 2 1 8
x 6 2

(2) 2 5 7
x 6 5

(3) 2 5 9
x 6 7

(4) 1 5 6
x 6 9

(5) 1 5 8
x 7 2

(6) 5 6 8
x 7 5

(7) 6 8 4
x 8 3

(8) 7 2 5
x 8 1

(9) 8 7 7
x 8 3

(10) 9 1 8
x 8 7

(11) 8 4 3
x 8 8

(12) 7 8 5
x 8 9

Exercise 75

(1) 1 6 4
x 4 4

(2) 1 7 4
x 4 5

(3) 1 5 2
x 4 6

(4) 2 3 3
x 4 7

(5) 2 1 5
x 4 8

(6) 1 5 3
x 4 9

(7) 1 6 4
x 5 0

(8) 1 7 3
x 5 2

(9) 1 8 4
x 5 6

(10) 1 8 6
x 5 7

(11) 1 3 7
x 5 8

(12) 1 2 9
x 6 1

Exercise 78

(1) 8 1 5
  x 9 2
———

(2) 7 2 7
  x 8 5
———

(3) 6 3 9
  x 7 7
———

(4) 9 2 6
  x 7 9
———

(5) 8 3 8
  x 8 2
———

(6) 7 6 8
  x 9 5
———

(7) 6 8 4
  x 7 3
———

(8) 8 2 5
  x 8 1
———

(9) 9 7 7
  x 9 3
———

(10) 8 1 8
  x 7 7
———

(11) 7 4 3
  x 8 8
———

(12) 6 8 5
  x 9 9
———

Exercise 77

(1) 9 6 1
  x 9 4
———

(2) 8 7 1
  x 8 5
———

(3) 7 2 2
  x 7 6
———

(4) 6 3 0
  x 7 7
———

(5) 8 1 2
  x 8 8
———

(6) 7 5 0
  x 9 9
———

(7) 6 6 1
  x 9 0
———

(8) 9 7 0
  x 8 2
———

(9) 7 8 1
  x 7 6
———

(10) 6 8 2
  x 9 7
———

(11) 9 3 4
  x 8 8
———

(12) 8 2 7
  x 7 1
———

Exercise 79 Decimals and Place Value

(1) $5.3 + 5.9$

(2) $24.2 + 56.9$

(3) $30.65 + 24.79$

(4) $1.19 + 232.1 + 6.4$

(5) $2.4 - 1.6$

(6) $28.1 - 19.3$

(7) $103.4 - 96.5$

(8) $18.12 - 2.4$

(9) 3.2×8

(10) 9.87×4

(11) 26.42×5

(12) 79.01×8

(13) $8.44 \div 4$

(14) $37.6 \div 2$

(15) $14.28 \div 7$

(16) $6 \div 5$

(17) £2.84 add £3.62

(18) £10.91 less £1.36

(19) £2.35 times 3

(20) £5.75 divided by 5

(21) 2m + 80 cm. Give your answer in m and cm.

(22) 3m - 150cm. Give your answer in cm.

(23) 85cm x 8. Give your answer in m and cm.

(24) 75cm ÷ 5. Give your answer in cm.

(25) 248kg + 982g. Give your answer in kg and g.

(26) 2kg - 699g. Give your answer in kg.

(27) 562g x 3. Give your answer in Kg and g.

(28) 3kg ÷ 4. Give your answer in g.

(29) 1 litre + 280 ml. Give your answer in litres and ml.

(30) 2 litres - 1200ml. Give your answer in ml.

(31) 625 ml x 7. Give your answer in litres and ml.

(32) 4 litres ÷ 5. Give your answer in ml.

(33) 65 minutes + 74 minutes. Give your answer in hours and minutes.

(34) 3 hours - 18 minutes. Give your answer in hours and minutes.

(35) 25 minutes x 6. Give your answer in hours and minutes.

(36) 2 hours 42 minutes ÷ 6. Give your answer in hours and minutes.

(37) 240 x 13

(38) 139 x 13

(39) 526 x 13

(40) 472 x 13

REMEMBER

£1.00 = 100p	1km = 1000m	1kg = 1000g	1 day = 24 hours
	1m = 100cm	1litre = 1000ml	1 hour = 60 min.
	1cm = 10mm		1 min. = 60 sec.

Exercise 80 Decimals and Place Value

(1) $6.3 + 8.9$

(2) $37.2 + 57.4$

(3) $87.65 + 56.76$

(4) $7.78 + 289.1 + 6.3$

(5) $5.9 - 4.2$

(6) $27.1 - 16.9$

(7) $189.4 - 94.5$

(8) $67.12 - 9.4$

(9) 8.2×6

(10) 9.87×8

(11) 34.56×9

(12) 95.09×8

(13) $7.35 \div 7$

(14) $49.6 \div 5$

(15) $19.38 \div 6$

(16) $8 \div 5$

(17) Total £3.85 and £10.64

(18) £15.99 take away £4.39

(19) £6.85 multiplied by 7

(20) Divide £1.75 by 5

(21) 5m plus 70 cm. Give your answer in m and cm.

(22) 9m less 250cm. Give your answer in cm.

(23) 4 times 36cm. Give your answer in m and cm.

(24) 95cm cut into 5 parts. Give your answer in cm.

(25) Find the total of 678kg and 999g. Give your answer in kg and g.

(26) Find the difference betwen 7kg and 999g. Give your answer in kg.

(27) Multiply 893g by 4. Give your answer in Kg and g.

(28) Share 12kg by 8. Give your answer in g.

(29) 3 litres plus 560 ml. Give your answer in litres and ml.

(30) 7 litres less 5200ml. Give your answer in ml.

(31) Eight times 425 ml. Give your answer in litres and ml.

(32) 3 litres shared between 5. Give your answer in ml.

(33) 85 minutes add 97 minutes. Give your answer in hours and minutes.

(34) 4 hours take away 57 minutes. Give your answer in hours and minutes.

(35) 8 times 23 minutes. Give your answer in hours and minutes.

(36) 8 hours 42 minutes ÷ 6. Give your answer in hours and minutes.

(37) 576 multiplied by 14

(38) 786 times 15

(39) Find the product of 432 and 16

(40) 942 times 17

REMEMBER

£1.00 = 100p	1km = 1000m	1kg = 1000g	1 day = 24 hours
	1m = 100cm	1litre = 1000ml	1 hour = 60 min.
	1cm = 10mm		1 min. = 60 sec.

Exercise 81 Decimals and Place Value

(1) 7 . 4 add 8 . 9

(2) 56 . 1 add 56 . 8

(3) Total 59 . 15 and 98 . 79

(4) 1 . 67 add 125 . 1 + and 8 . 4

(5) 9 . 7 take 6 . 6

(6) 56 . 1 less 49 . 3

(7) Decrease 128 . 4 by 35 . 9

(8) 79 . 13 subtract 9 . 7

(9) 8 . 2 times 7

(10) 4 . 97 multiplied by 8

(11) Multiply 78 . 42 by 4

(12) 93 . 01 multiplied by 5

(13) 3 . 49 divided by 8

(14) 69 . 6 shared between 6

(15) 18 . 66 split into 6parts.

(16) 8 divided by 5

(17) £9 . 34 plus £8 . 02

(18) £8 . 71 less £6. 36

(19) £6 . 75 times 4

(20) £8 . 35 divided by 5

(21) Total 5m and 67 cm. Give your answer in m and cm.

(22) 39m minus 560cm. Give your answer in cm.

(23) 34cm multiplied by 9. Give your answer in m and cm.

(24) 95cm shared by 5. Give your answer in cm.

(25) 278kg plus 777g. Give your answer in kg and g.

(26) 9kg take away 759g. Give your answer in kg.

(27) What is the product of 892g and 5. Give your answer in Kg and g.

(28) 7kg divided by 4. Give your answer in g.

(29) Sum 8 litres and 670 ml. Give your answer in litres and ml.

(30) 7 litres less 1800ml. Give your answer in ml.

(31) 834 ml multiplied by 7. Give your answer in litres and ml.

(32) Divide 7 litres by 5. Give your answer in ml.

(33) 89 minutes plus 97 minutes. Give your answer in hours and minutes.

(34) 9 hours minus 34 minutes. Give your answer in hours and minutes.

(35) 93 minutes multiplied by 8. Give your answer in hours and minutes.

(36) 8 hours 48 minutes divided by 6. Answer in hours and minutes.

(37) 258 x 24

(38) 149 x 36

(39) 352 x 49

(40) 442 x 87

REMEMBER			
£1 . 00 = 100p	1km = 1000m	1kg = 1000g	1 day = 24 hours
	1m = 100cm	1litre = 1000ml	1 hour = 60 min.
	1cm = 10mm		1 min. = 60 sec.

Exercise 82 Decimals and Place Value

(1) 9 . 4 + 8 . 2

(2) 74 . 1 + 75 . 9

(3) 37 . 34 + 81 . 77

(4) 4 . 72 + 255 . 1 + 6 . 9

(5) 7 . 4 - 5 . 6

(6) 81 . 1 - 79 . 3

(7) 106 . 4 - 45 . 5

(8) 11 . 17 - 3 . 4

(9) 7 . 2 x 7

(10) 9 . 22 x 5

(11) 67 . 42 x 3

(12) 89 . 71 x 9

(13) 7 . 44 ÷ 7

(14) 87 . 6 ÷ 6

(15) 28 . 26 ÷ 6

(16) 9 ÷ 5

(17) £4 . 94 add £8 . 62

(18) £19 . 91 less £1 . 88

(19) £7 . 35 times 8

(20) £81 . 75 divided by 5

(21) 4m + 67 cm. Give your answer in m and cm.

(22) 9m - 50cm. Give your answer in cm.

(23) 35cm x 7. Give your answer in m and cm.

(24) 175cm ÷ 5. Give your answer in cm.

(25) 548kg + 882g. Give your answer in kg and g.

(26) 7kg - 1499g. Give your answer in kg.

(27) 888g x 3. Give your answer in Kg and g.

(28) 9kg ÷ 4. Give your answer in g.

(29) 6 litre + 1270 ml. Give your answer in litres and ml.

(30) 4 litres - 1800ml. Give your answer in ml.

(31) 328 ml x 9. Give your answer in litres and ml.

(32) 9 litres ÷ 5. Give your answer in ml.

(33) 69 minutes + 39 minutes. Give your answer in hours and minutes.

(34) 7 hours - 26 minutes. Give your answer in hours and minutes.

(35) 56 minutes x 7. Give your answer in hours and minutes.

(36) 8 hours 42 minutes ÷ 6. Give your answer in hours and minutes.

(37) 894 x 65

(38) 847 x 73

(39) 927 x 85

(40) 998 x 99

REMEMBER

£1 . 00 = 100p	1km = 1000m	1kg = 1000g	1 day = 24 hours
	1m = 100cm	1litre = 1000ml	1 hour = 60 min.
	1cm = 10mm		1 min. = 60 sec.

Exercise 83 Decimals and Place Value

(1) 5 . 3 + 6 . 7

(2) 89 . 2 + 58 . 9

(3) 22 . 98 + 78 . 16

(4) 1 . 99 + 989 . 1 + 8 . 4

(5) 1 6 . 9 - 8 . 2

(6) 29 . 1 - 14 . 9

(7) 1225 . 4 - 97 . 5

(8) 55 . 12 - 12 . 4

(9) 9 . 5 x 8

(10) 3 . 87 x 9

(11) 36 . 16 x 7

(12) 101 . 09 x 9

(13) 89 . 32 ÷ 7

(14) 46 . 5 ÷ 5

(15) 27 . 36 ÷ 6

(16) 9 ÷ 5

(17) Total £37 . 95 and £101 . 84

(18) £175 . 09 take away £16 . 39

(19) £6 8. 85 multiplied by 7

(20) Divide £10 . 75 by 5

(21) 7m plus 77 cm. Give your answer in m and cm.

(22) 3m less 299cm. Give your answer in cm.

(23) 9 times 76cm . Give your answer in m and cm.

(24) 105cm cut into 5 parts. Give your answer in cm.

(25) Find the total of 342kg and 229g. Give your answer in kg and g.

(26) Find the difference betwen 4kg and 233g. Give your answer in kg.

(27) Multiply 1093g by 6. Give your answer in Kg and g.

(28) Share 120kg by 8. Give your an swer in g.

(29) 9 litres plus 960 ml. Give your an swer in litres and ml.

(30) 5.5 litres less 5200ml. Give your answer in ml.

(31) Nine times 825 ml. Give your answer in litres and ml.

(32) 9 litres shared between 5. Give your answer in ml.

(33) 165 minutes add 94 minutes. Give your answer in hours and minutes.

(34) 9 hours take away 57 minutes. Give your answer in hours and minutes.

(35) 7 times 47 minutes. Give your answer in hours and minutes.

(36) 9 hours 24 minutes ÷ 6. Give your answer in hours and minutes.

(37) 873 multiplied by 97

(38) 639 times 75

(39) Find the product of 927 and 69

(40) 996 times 87

REMEMBER

£1 . 00 = 100p	1km = 1000m	1kg = 1000g	1 day = 24 hours
	1m = 100cm	1litre = 1000ml	1 hour = 60 min.
	1cm = 10mm		1 min. = 60 sec.

Exercise 84 Decimals and Place Value

(1)   19 . 2 add 6 . 9

(2)   423 . 1 add 59 . 8

(3)   Total 66 . 15 and 192 . 79

(4)   1 . 77 add 225 . 1 + and 9 . 4

(5)   19 . 7 take 13 . 6

(6)   56 . 1 less 29 . 3

(7)   Decrease 156 . 4 by 99 . 9

(8)   83 . 13 subtract 16 . 7

(9)   18 . 2 times 8

(10)   94 . 97 multiplied by 6

(11)   Multiply 178 . 42 by 8

(12)   44 . 01 multiplied by 6

(13)   14 . 48 divided by 8

(14)   669 . 6 shared between 6

(15)   184 . 24 split into 8 parts.

(16)   14 divided by 5

(17)   £94 . 34 plus £87 . 02

(18)   £89 . 71 less £64. 36

(19)   £67 . 75 times 4

(20)   £8 6. 35 divided by 5

(21)   Total 15m and 167 cm. Give your answer in m and cm.

(22)   27m minus 960cm. Give your answer in cm.

(23)   56cm multiplied by 9. Give your answer in m and cm.

(24)   75cm shared by 5. Give your answer in cm.

(25)   348kg plus 567g. Give your answer in kg and g.

(26)   8kg take away 459g. Give your answer in kg.

(27)   What is the product of 742g and 6. Give your answer in Kg and g.

(28)   17kg divided by 4. Give your answer in g.

(29)   Sum 9 litres and 1670 ml. Give your answer in litres and ml.

(30)   4 litres less 2600ml. Give your answer in ml.

(31)   934 ml multiplied by 9. Give your answer in litres and ml.

(32)   Divide 17.5 litres by 5. Give your answer in ml.

(33)   189 minutes plus 971 minutes. Give your answer in hours and minutes.

(34)   11 hours minus 75 minutes. Give your answer in hours and minutes.

(35)   235 minutes multiplied by 8. Give your answer in hours and minutes.

(36)   6 hours 24 minutes divided by 6. Answer in hours and minutes.

(37)   836 x 43

(38)   832 x 84

(39)   839 x 65

(40)   842 x 29

REMEMBER

£1 . 00 = 100p	1km = 1000m	1kg = 1000g	1 day = 24 hours
	1m = 100cm	1litre = 1000ml	1 hour = 60 min.
	1cm = 10mm		1 min. = 60 sec.

Exercise 85 Decimals and Place Value

(1) 7 . 3 + 8 . 7

(2) 72 . 2 + 57 . 9

(3) 32 . 98 + 98 . 16

(4) 6 . 99 + 229 . 1 + 3 . 4

(5) 11 . 9 - 4 . 2

(6) 19 . 1 - 12 . 4

(7) 3325 . 4 - 193 . 5

(8) 43 . 12 - 18 . 4

(9) 4 . 5 x 7

(10) 6 . 27 x 8

(11) 48 . 16 x 6

(12) 99 . 09 x 9

(13) 34 . 38 ÷ 6

(14) 89 . 55 ÷ 5

(15) 64 . 38 ÷ 6

(16) 8 ÷ 5

(17) Total £89 . 95 and £134 . 24

(18) £672 . 09 take away £16 9. 39

(19) £682. 85 multiplied by 8

(20) Divide £47 . 75 by 5

(21) 17m plus 7 cm. Give your answer in m and cm.

(22) 15m less 56cm. Give your answer in cm.

(23) 3 times 96cm . Give your answer in m and cm.

(24) 88cm cut into 8 parts. Give your answer in cm.

(25) Find the total of 366kg and 211g. Give your answer in kg and g.

(26) Find the difference betwen 8kg and 532g. Give your answer in kg.

(27) Multiply 1765g by 7. Give your answer in Kg and g.

(28) Share 640kg by 8. Give your an swer in g.

(29) 7 litres plus 660 ml. Give your an swer in litres and ml.

(30) 5.8 litres less 5700ml. Give your answer in ml.

(31) Nine times 776 ml. Give your answer in litres and ml.

(32) 7 litres shared between 5. Give your answer in ml.

(33) 123 minutes add 84 minutes. Give your answer in hours and minutes.

(34) 6 hours take away 54 minutes. Give your answer in hours and minutes.

(35) 6 times 45 minutes. Give your answer in hours and minutes.

(36) 8 hours 30 minutes ÷ 6. Give your answer in hours and minutes.

(37) 563 multiplied by 57

(38) 899 times 85

(39) Find the product of 757 and 89

(40) 896 times 88

REMEMBER

£1 . 00 = 100p   1km = 1000m   1kg = 1000g   1 day = 24 hours

                     1m = 100cm   1litre = 1000ml   1 hour = 60 min.

                     1cm = 10mm   1 min. = 60 sec.

Exercise 86 Decimals and Place Value

(1) 15 . 2 add 8 . 9

(2) 222 . 1 add 87 . 8

(3) Total 78 . 15 and 333 . 79

(4) 8 . 97 add 65 . 1 plus 4 . 4

(5) 54 . 7 take 19 . 7

(6) 43 . 8 less 33 . 3

(7) Decrease 274 . 4 by 67 . 9

(8) 43 . 19 subtract 13 . 8

(9) 29 . 2 times 9

(10) 88 . 67 multiplied by 7

(11) Multiply 368 . 42 by 9

(12) 48 . 91 multiplied by 7

(13) 16 . 54 divided by 8

(14) 366 . 6 shared between 6

(15) 64 . 64 split into 8 parts.

(16) 18 divided by 5

(17) £184 . 34 plus £167 . 02

(18) £97 . 61 less £54. 96

(19) £88 . 75 times 4

(20) £156. 35 divided by 5

(21) Total 19m and 897 cm. Give your answer in m and cm.

(22) 11m minus 987cm. Give your answer in cm.

(23) 48cm multiplied by 8. Give your answer in m and cm.

(24) 90cm shared by 5. Give your answer in cm.

(25) 875kg plus 293g. Give your answer in kg and g.

(26) 6kg take away 599g. Give your answer in kg.

(27) What is the product of 888g and 6. Give your answer in Kg and g.

(28) 19kg divided by 8. Give your answer in g.

(29) Sum 5 litres and 1670 ml. Give your answer in litres and ml.

(30) 9 litres less 7900ml. Give your answer in ml.

(31) 564 ml multiplied by 7. Give your answer in litres and ml.

(32) Divide 13.5 litres by 5. Give your answer in ml.

(33) 279 minutes plus 571 minutes. Give your answer in hours and minutes.

(34) 16 hours minus 85 minutes. Give your answer in hours and minutes.

(35) 185 minutes multiplied by 9. Give your answer in hours and minutes.

(36) 9 hours 36 minutes divided by 6. Answer in hours and minutes.

(37) 936 x 93

(38) 703 x 87

(39) 238 x 95

(40) 878 x 79

REMEMBER

£1 . 00 = 100p	1km = 1000m	1kg = 1000g	1 day = 24 hours
	1m = 100cm	1litre = 1000ml	1 hour = 60 min.
	1cm = 10mm		1 min. = 60 sec.

ANSWERS

Diagnostic Test
(1) 49
(2) 49
(3) 48
(4) 40
(5) 40
(6) 40
(7) 388
(8) 399
(9) 399
(10) 240
(11) 240
(12) 260
(13) 10
(14) 12
(15) 11
(16) 9
(17) 7
(18) 8
(19) 111
(20) 113
(21) 111
(22) 118
(23) 108
(24) 39
(25) 24
(26) 26
(27) 28
(28) 50
(29) 52
(30) 54
(31) 286
(32) 268
(33) 260
(34) 450
(35) 474
(36) 418
(37) 01
(38) 02
(39) 03
(40) 100
(41) 111
(42) 112
(43) 11r1
(44) 12r1
(45) 13r1
(46) 111r1
(47) 122r1
(48) 133r1
(49) 18
(50) 27
(51) 36
(52) 108
(53) 109
(54) 116
(55) 16r1
(56) 17r1
(57) 18r1
(58) 089r1
(59) 265r1
(60) 359r1
(61) 118
(62) 221
(63) 1330
(64) 106
(65) 4576
(66) 3216
(67) 7280
(68) 239.69
(69) 2m80cm
(70) 800ml

Exercise 1
(1) 49
(2) 49
(3) 48
(4) 48
(5) 56
(6) 58
(7) 68
(8) 68
(9) 51
(10) 53
(11) 55
(12) 57
(13) 65
(14) 67
(15) 69
(16) 67

Exercise 2
(1) 79
(2) 59
(3) 62
(4) 64
(5) 83
(6) 85
(7) 87
(8) 66
(9) 93
(10) 95
(11) 87
(12) 89
(13) 48
(14) 48
(15) 48
(16) 48

Exercise 3
(1) 75
(2) 77
(3) 79
(4) 77
(5) 99
(6) 99
(7) 98
(8) 94
(9) 99
(10) 97

Exercise 4
(1) 40
(2) 40
(3) 40
(4) 40
(5) 50
(6) 50
(7) 51
(8) 53
(9) 60
(10) 71
(11) 70
(12) 81
(13) 81
(14) 73
(15) 73
(16) 75

Exercise 5
(1) 80
(2) 84
(3) 83
(4) 91
(5) 70
(6) 72
(7) 74
(8) 74
(9) 102
(10) 101
(11) 104
(12) 111
(13) 101
(14) 103
(15) 123
(16) 125

Exercise 6
(1) 107
(2) 110
(3) 115
(4) 117
(5) 110
(6) 112
(7) 114
(8) 116
(9) 114
(10) 119
(11) 121
(12) 110
(13) 111
(14) 114
(15) 123
(16) 127

Exercise 7
(1) 388
(2) 399
(3) 399
(4) 848
(5) 985
(6) 889
(7) 756
(8) 759
(9) 889
(10) 577
(11) 599
(12) 589

Exercise 8
(1) 659
(2) 789
(3) 849
(4) 769
(5) 997
(6) 699
(7) 737
(8) 879
(9) 996
(10) 989
(11) 895
(12) 999

Exercise 9
(1) 934
(2) 948
(3) 996
(4) 879
(5) 889
(6) 993
(7) 979
(8) 936
(9) 959
(10) 999
(11) 987
(12) 978

Exercise 10
(1) 240
(2) 240
(3) 260
(4) 270
(5) 271
(6) 241
(7) 461
(8) 445
(9) 453
(10) 363
(11) 366
(12) 364

Exercise 11
(1) 510
(2) 510
(3) 510
(4) 511
(5) 531
(6) 521
(7) 613
(8) 642
(9) 670
(10) 610
(11) 612
(12) 656

Exercise 12
(1) 1117
(2) 1110
(3) 1310
(4) 1012
(5) 1001
(6) 1121
(7) 1013
(8) 1031
(9) 1600
(10) 1370
(11) 1550
(12) 1798

ANSWERS

Exercise 13
(1) 10
(2) 12
(3) 11
(4) 11
(5) 11
(6) 13
(7) 13
(8) 14
(9) 12
(10) 20
(11) 11
(12) 21
(13) 21
(14) 12
(15) 13
(16) 13

Exercise 16
(1) 09
(2) 07
(3) 08
(4) 09
(5) 08
(6) 09
(7) 10
(8) 08
(9) 05
(10) 14
(11) 06
(12) 19
(13) 16
(14) 09
(15) 19
(16) 09

Exercise 19
(1) 111
(2) 113
(3) 111
(4) 112
(5) 113
(6) 111
(7) 102
(8) 216
(9) 108
(10) 123
(11) 120
(12) 153

Exercise 22
(1) 118
(2) 108
(3) 039
(4) 119
(5) 117
(6) 058
(7) 208
(8) 118
(9) 134
(10) 117
(11) 144
(12) 276

Exercise 25
(1) 24
(2) 26
(3) 28
(4) 22
(5) 40
(6) 42
(7) 44
(8) 46
(9) 48
(10) 60
(11) 62
(12) 64
(13) 66
(14) 68
(15) 84
(16) 88

Exercise 14
(1) 13
(2) 30
(3) 32
(4) 31
(5) 21
(6) 33
(7) 33
(8) 33
(9) 24
(10) 21
(11) 32
(12) 12
(13) 43
(14) 43
(15) 12
(16) 34

Exercise 17
(1) 01
(2) 13
(3) 07
(4) 16
(5) 19
(6) 19
(7) 07
(8) 19
(9) 19
(10) 21
(11) 22
(12) 23
(13) 16
(14) 25
(15) 09
(16) 18

Exercise 20
(1) 123
(2) 211
(3) 120
(4) 210
(5) 201
(6) 264
(7) 112
(8) 221
(9) 331
(10) 426
(11) 351
(12) 100

Exercise 23
(1) 181
(2) 131
(3) 265
(4) 071
(5) 042
(6) 302
(7) 081
(8) 365
(9) 391
(10) 192
(11) 281
(12) 381

Exercise 26
(1) 30
(2) 33
(3) 36
(4) 39
(5) 60
(6) 63
(7) 66
(8) 69
(9) 90
(10) 93
(11) 96
(12) 99
(13) 03
(14) 06
(15) 09
(16) 123

Exercise 15
(1) 21
(2) 31
(3) 12
(4) 10
(5) 42
(6) 21
(7) 42
(8) 17
(9) 56
(10) 20
(11) 50
(12) 11
(13) 23
(14) 21
(15) 14
(16) 52

Exercise 18
(1) 28
(2) 29
(3) 09
(4) 11
(5) 09
(6) 19
(7) 39
(8) 47
(9) 49
(10) 07
(11) 19
(12) 39
(13) 19
(14) 29
(15) 03
(16) 35

Exercise 21
(1) 222
(2) 104
(3) 321
(4) 132
(5) 331
(6) 243
(7) 263
(8) 412
(9) 627
(10) 622
(11) 201
(12) 134

Exercise 24
(1) 049
(2) 059
(3) 079
(4) 089
(5) 293
(6) 159
(7) 274
(8) 399
(9) 169
(10) 589
(11) 468
(12) 563

Exercise 27
(1) 40
(2) 50
(3) 60
(4) 70
(5) 80
(6) 90
(7) 44
(8) 48
(9) 55
(10) 66
(11) 77
(12) 88
(13) 99
(14) 04
(15) 08
(16) 07

ANSWERS

Exercise28
(1) 50
(2) 52
(3) 54
(4) 56
(5) 58
(6) 70
(7) 72
(8) 74
(9) 76
(10) 78
(11) 90
(12) 92
(13) 94
(14) 96
(15) 98
(16) 110

Exercise 29
(1) 72
(2) 75
(3) 78
(4) 81
(5) 84
(6) 87
(7) 102
(8) 105
(9) 108
(10) 111
(11) 114
(12) 117
(13) 132
(14) 135
(15) 138
(16) 141

Exercise 30
(1) 52
(2) 56
(3) 60
(4) 64
(5) 68
(6) 72
(7) 76
(8) 92
(9) 60
(10) 65
(11) 70
(12) 75
(13) 72
(14) 78
(15) 98
(16) 105

Exercise 31
(1) 286
(2) 268
(3) 260
(4) 488
(5) 484
(6) 486
(7) 684
(8) 664
(9) 666
(10) 884
(11) 844
(12) 848

Exercise 32
(1) 309
(2) 369
(3) 390
(4) 690
(5) 633
(6) 669
(7) 999
(8) 963
(9) 900
(10) 933
(11) 966
(12) 909

Exercise 33
(1) 404
(2) 484
(3) 488
(4) 880
(5) 848
(6) 500
(7) 505
(8) 600
(9) 666
(10) 777
(11) 800
(12) 909

Exercise 34
(1) 450
(2) 474
(3) 418
(4) 252
(5) 276
(6) 456
(7) 642
(8) 675
(9) 621
(10) 924
(11) 492
(12) 460

Exercise35
(1) 312
(2) 354
(3) 596
(4) 732
(5) 462
(6) 795
(7) 532
(8) 500
(9) 904
(10) 675
(11) 610
(12) 670

Exercise 36
(1) 738
(2) 2538
(3) 1980
(4) 3710
(5) 4977
(6) 4361
(7) 2664
(8) 6568
(9) 7200
(10) 7299
(11) 6498
(12) 8127

Exercise 37
(1) 01
(2) 02
(3) 03
(4) 04
(5) 10
(6) 20
(7) 30
(8) 40
(9) 11
(10) 12
(11) 13
(12) 14
(13) 21
(14) 22
(15) 23
(16) 24
(17) 31
(18) 32
(19) 34
(20) 33

Exercise 38
(1) 41
(2) 42
(3) 43
(4) 44
(5) 01
(6) 02
(7) 03
(8) 10
(9) 11
(10) 20
(11) 30
(12) 12
(13) 13
(14) 21
(15) 22
(16) 23
(17) 31
(18) 32
(19) 33
(20) 10

Exercise 39
(1) 01
(2) 02
(3) 10
(4) 20
(5) 11
(6) 12
(7) 21
(8) 22
(9) 01
(10) 10
(11) 11
(12) 01
(13) 10
(14) 11
(15) 01
(16) 10
(17) 11
(18) 01
(19) 10
(20) 11

Exercise 40
(1) 100
(2) 111
(3) 112
(4) 113
(5) 114
(6) 122
(7) 123
(8) 124
(9) 133
(10) 134
(11) 210
(12) 211
(13) 230
(14) 241
(15) 231
(16) 301
(17) 331
(18) 322
(19) 344
(20) 443

Exercise 41
(1) 100
(2) 110
(3) 111
(4) 112
(5) 113
(6) 101
(7) 102
(8) 103
(9) 120
(10) 123
(11) 201
(12) 202
(13) 203
(14) 210
(15) 211
(16) 212
(17) 310
(18) 311
(19) 312
(20) 333

Exercise 42
(1) 100
(2) 101
(3) 111
(4) 011
(5) 001
(6) 110
(7) 102
(8) 120
(9) 201
(10) 210
(11) 211
(12) 212
(13) 221
(14) 122
(15) 202
(16) 220
(17) 022
(18) 101
(19) 110
(20) 111

ANSWERS

Exercise 43
(1) 11r1
(2) 12r1
(3) 13r1
(4) 14r1
(5) 21r1
(6) 22r1
(7) 23r1
(8) 24r1
(9) 31r1
(10) 32r1
(11) 33r1
(12) 34r1
(13) 41r1
(14) 42r1
(15) 43r1
(16) 44r1
(17) 10r1
(18) 20r1
(19) 30r1
(20) 40r1

Exercise 46
(1) 111r1
(2) 122r1
(3) 133r1
(4) 144r1
(5) 121r1
(6) 132r1
(7) 143r1
(8) 114r1
(9) 131r1
(10) 142r1
(11) 113r1
(12) 124r1
(13) 141r1
(14) 112r1
(15) 123r1
(16) 134r1
(17) 110r1
(18) 120r1
(19) 340r1
(20) 430r1

Exercise 49
(1) 18
(2) 27
(3) 36
(4) 49
(5) 14
(6) 18
(7) 25
(8) 29
(9) 13
(10) 16
(11) 18
(12) 03
(13) 13
(14) 15
(15) 16
(16) 02
(17) 13
(18) 14
(19) 16
(20) 03

Exercise 52
(1) 108
(2) 109
(3) 116
(4) 126
(5) 127
(6) 136
(7) 138
(8) 139
(9) 092
(10) 073
(11) 161
(12) 172
(13) 262
(14) 293
(15) 374
(16) 391
(17) 266
(18) 166
(19) 369
(20) 276

Exercise 55
(1) 16r1
(2) 17r1
(3) 18r1
(4) 19r1
(5) 25r1
(6) 27r1
(7) 35r1
(8) 37r1
(9) 45r1
(10) 46r1
(11) 48r1
(12) 07r1
(13) 09r1
(14) 13r2
(15) 15r2
(16) 16
(17) 17r1
(18) 17r2
(19) 24r2
(20) 29r1

Exercise 44
(1) 11r1
(2) 12r1
(3) 11r2
(4) 12r2
(5) 21r1
(6) 22r1
(7) 21r2
(8) 22r2
(9) 31r1
(10) 32r1
(11) 31r2
(12) 32r2
(13) 10r1
(14) 10r2
(15) 20r1
(16) 20r2
(17) 30r1
(18) 30r2
(19) 11r1
(20) 11r2

Exercise 47
(1) 111r1
(2) 111r2
(3) 112r1
(4) 112r2
(5) 121r1
(6) 121r2
(7) 122r1
(8) 122r2
(9) 131r1
(10) 131r2
(11) 132r1
(12) 132r2
(13) 211r1
(14) 211r2
(15) 212r1
(16) 212r2
(17) 321r1
(18) 321r2
(19) 322r1
(20) 322r2

Exercise 50
(1) 27
(2) 26
(3) 18
(4) 16
(5) 06
(6) 18
(7) 17
(8) 14
(9) 02
(10) 17
(11) 14
(12) 13
(13) 12
(14) 03
(15) 14
(16) 16
(17) 12
(18) 13
(19) 02
(20) 05

Exercise 53
(1) 114
(2) 118
(3) 126
(4) 225
(5) 207
(6) 205
(7) 316
(8) 329
(9) 071
(10) 141
(11) 191
(12) 262
(13) 282
(14) 062
(15) 073
(16) 093
(17) 176
(18) 246
(19) 275
(20) 046

Exercise 56
(1) 15r3
(2) 18r3
(3) 20r3
(4) 23r1
(5) 13r2
(6) 15r1
(7) 18r1
(8) 08r1
(9) 22r1
(10) 24r1
(11) 04r4
(12) 13r3
(13) 14r3
(14) 16r4
(15) 17r4
(16) 19r2
(17) 06r1
(18) 09r2
(19) 10r2
(20) 12r3

Exercise 45
(1) 11r1
(2) 11r2
(3) 11r3
(4) 12r1
(5) 21r1
(6) 21r2
(7) 21r3
(8) 22r1
(9) 10r1
(10) 10r2
(11) 10r3
(12) 20r1
(13) 20r2
(14) 20r3
(15) 11r1
(16) 11r2
(17) 11r3
(18) 11r4
(19) 10r1
(20) 10r2

Exercise 48
(1) 111r1
(2) 111r2
(3) 111r3
(4) 112r1
(5) 121r1
(6) 121r2
(7) 121r3
(8) 122r1
(9) 221r1
(10) 221r2
(11) 221r3
(12) 222r1
(13) 110r1
(14) 110r2
(15) 110r3
(16) 120r1
(17) 120r2
(18) 120r3
(19) 220r1
(20) 220r2

Exercise 51
(1) 05
(2) 07
(3) 08
(4) 12
(5) 04
(6) 05
(7) 07
(8) 09
(9) 06
(10) 08
(11) 09
(12) 12
(13) 12
(14) 04
(15) 05
(16) 07
(17) 02
(18) 03
(19) 04
(20) 05

Exercise 54
(1) 082
(2) 061
(3) 042
(4) 117
(5) 130
(6) 134
(7) 135
(8) 138
(9) 171
(10) 164
(11) 173
(12) 159
(13) 182
(14) 187
(15) 189
(16) 196
(17) 247
(18) 236
(19) 248
(20) 245

Exercise 57
(1) 12r1
(2) 12r3
(3) 13r3
(4) 13r5
(5) 14r3
(6) 15r1
(7) 11r5
(8) 12r1
(9) 12r5
(10) 13r2
(11) 08r6
(12) 03r4
(13) 11r1
(14) 11r4
(15) 03r3
(16) 06r5
(17) 10r2
(18) 10r7
(19) 04r2
(20) 07r8

ANSWERS

Exercise 58
(1) 089r1
(2) 265r1
(3) 359r1
(4) 177r1
(5) 263r1
(6) 365r1
(7) 446r1
(8) 373r1
(9) 183r2
(10) 247r1
(11) 290r1
(12) 324
(13) 047r1
(14) 075r2
(15) 297r2
(16) 248r2
(17) 181r1
(18) 084r3
(19) 132r1
(20) 192r3

Exercise 59
(1) 086r2
(2) 072r1
(3) 057r4
(4) 154r4
(5) 136r1
(6) 164r4
(7) 198r1
(8) 024r3
(9) 052r3
(10) 117
(11) 073r5
(12) 020r3
(13) 068r3
(14) 045r4
(15) 016r3
(16) 127r2
(17) 104r6
(18) 137r5
(19) 121r6
(20) 060r2

Exercise 60
(1) 123r7
(2) 123r3
(3) 120r1
(4) 085r7
(5) 070r1
(6) 096r6
(7) 026r5
(8) 110r3
(9) 028r2
(10) 039r7
(11) 110r3
(12) 080r4
(13) 096
(14) 073r6
(15) 060r2
(16) 013r2
(17) 025r4
(18) 085r5
(19) 026r2
(20) 082r2

Exercise 61
(1) 1161
(2) 1222
(3) 1710
(4) 1556
(5) 154
(6) 548
(7) 336
(8) 081
(9) 884
(10) 1962
(11) 2888
(12) 1845
(13) 322
(14) 322r2
(15) 119r3
(16) 167r2
(17) 118
(18) 221
(19) 1330
(20) 106
(21) 255
(22) 321
(23) 5348
(24) 48
(25) 6672
(26) 267
(27) 14,220
(28) 908
(29) 4730
(30) 357
(31) 216
(32) 387
(33) 9700
(34) 2700
(35) 22730
(36) 346
(37) 7003
(38) 4124
(39) 58851
(40) 909

Exercise 62
(1) 686
(2) 1749
(3) 1383
(4) 1929
(5) 131
(6) 416
(7) 415
(8) 185
(9) 246
(10) 1035
(11) 3368
(12) 2645
(13) 143
(14) 043
(15) 155r1
(16) 198
(17) 109
(18) 134
(19) 1024
(20) 157

(21) 192
(22) 550
(23) 3648
(24) 113
(25) 7785
(26) 68
(27) 27132
(28) 913
(29) 5941
(30) 229
(31) 294
(32) 1402
(33) 2931
(34) 1800
(35) 32628
(36) 776
(37) 6251
(38) 4170
(39) 45504
(40) 631

Exercise 63
(1) 1028
(2) 1013
(3) 1256
(4) 1227
(5) 501
(6) 219
(7) 145
(8) 081
(9) 484
(10) 1460
(11) 4338
(12) 5607
(13) 332
(14) 241
(15) 144
(16) 098r1
(17) 1184
(18) 28
(19) 276
(20) 210
(21) 590
(22) 12
(23) 3954
(24) 14
(25) 5004
(26) 119
(27) 39704
(28) 755
(29) 1065
(30) 170
(31) 300
(32) 108r4
(33) 15575
(34) 7595
(35) 4512
(36) 500
(37) 7404
(38) 200
(39) 3468
(40) 150

Exercise 64
(1) 691
(2) 1551
(3) 1772
(4) 1616
(5) 121
(6) 181
(7) 089
(8) 13
(9) 444
(10) 702
(11) 2500
(12) 3645
(13) 432
(14) 103
(15) 052
(16) 149
(17) 1559
(18) 633
(19) 2736
(20) 20
(21) 3696
(22) 288
(23) 684
(24) 84r5
(25) 2664
(26) 7798
(27) 4495
(28) 421
(29) 438
(30) 220
(31) 3300
(32) 140
(33) 146
(34) 101
(35) 1000
(36) 097
(37) 15953
(38) 1120
(39) 24054
(40) 099

Exercise 65
(1) 1160
(2) 1207
(3) 1717
(4) 1559
(5) 456
(6) 141
(7) 011
(8) 308
(9) 675
(10) 2524
(11) 4320
(12) 2513
(13) 421
(14) 231r1
(15) 080r1
(16) 131r3
(17) 7437
(18) 208
(19) 3378
(20) 71

(21) 244
(22) 112
(23) 1780
(24) 49
(25) 79754
(26) 465
(27) 30396
(28) 1777
(29) 17632
(30) 400
(31) 336
(32) 70
(33) 14366
(34) 1234
(35) 9520
(36) 0723
(37) 5036
(38) 4520
(39) 41247
(40) 0632

Exercise 66
(1) 687
(2) 1764
(3) 1849
(4) 2035
(5) 556
(6) 542
(7) 191
(8) 59
(9) 666
(10) 1705
(11) 3420
(12) 3160
(13) 431r1
(14) 183
(15) 161
(16) 62
(17) 1648
(18) 469
(19) 3969
(20) 120
(21) 725
(22) 851
(23) 6601
(24) 142
(25) 5568
(26) 499
(27) 14070
(28) 1124
(29) 8367
(30) 190
(31) 343
(32) 725
(33) 8497
(34) 3703
(35) 43584
(36) 0964
(37) 2553
(38) 6
(39) 45504
(40) 157927

ANSWERS

Exercise 67
(1) 825
(2) 1609
(3) 1859
(4) 774
(5) 302
(6) 79
(7) 45
(8) 147
(9) 1100
(10) 1235
(11) 4500
(12) 2220
(13) 123
(14) 41
(15) 92r5
(16) 051
(17) 936
(18) 323
(19) 1729
(20) 317
(21) 663
(22) 907
(23) 1760
(24) 144
(25) 1456
(26) 335
(27) 20736
(28) 123457
(29) 24751
(30) 264
(31) 603
(32) 350
(33) 1632
(34) 4999
(35) 12345678910
(36) 130r6
(37) 10019
(38) 25
(39) 28416
(40) 615r3

Exercise 68
(1) 993
(2) 583
(3) 1128
(4) 2189
(5) 92
(6) 569
(7) 458
(8) 351
(9) 500
(10) 2528
(11) 5720
(12) 5751
(13) 82r2
(14) 83r1
(15) 177r3
(16) 55r1
(17) 1462
(18) 638
(19) 555
(20) 247

(21) 787
(22) 158
(23) 3752
(24) 195
(25) 1040
(26) 550
(27) 1712
(28) 12345
(29) 1260
(30) 211
(31) 3356
(32) 323r1
(33) 770
(34) 495
(35) 3078
(36) 246
(37) 787
(38) 225
(39) 1953
(40) 32255

Exercise 69
(1) 863
(2) 1453
(3) 1808
(4) 1533
(5) 162
(6) 159
(7) 208
(8) 011
(9) 4125
(10) 4992
(11) 2625
(12) 1431
(13) 222r1
(14) 179r4
(15) 073
(16) 022
(17) 1132
(18) 650
(19) 2695
(20) 217r3
(21) 954
(22) 398
(23) 2288
(24) 669
(25) 716
(26) 148
(27) 1968
(28) 1079
(29) 835
(30) 474
(31) 3740
(32) 4937
(33) 866
(34) 505
(35) 3536
(36) 216
(37) 1375
(38) 67
(39) 3936
(40) 224355

Exercise 70
(1) 999
(2) 1617
(3) 1530
(4) 2007
(5) 106
(6) 485
(7) 623
(8) 426
(9) 1595
(10) 3906
(11) 2667
(12) 4149
(13) 52
(14) 252r1
(15) 76r7
(16) 37r3
(17) 1292
(18) 949
(19) 1516
(20) 169r3
(21) 1315
(22) 261
(23) 6651
(24) 142r5
(25) 497
(26) 814
(27) 2790
(28) 12345
(29) 1983
(30) 909
(31) 4046
(32) 119r2
(33) 1350
(34) 722
(35) 0
(36) 171r3
(37) 5432
(38) 7928
(39) 12156
(40) 441

Exercise 71
(1) 3864
(2) 4275
(3) 3172
(4) 6210
(5) 5936
(6) 4350
(7) 4830
(8) 5440
(9) 6516
(10) 6734
(11) 5092
(12) 5207

Exercise 72
(1) 9030
(2) 10215
(3) 11233
(4) 6174
(5) 7176
(6) 14740
(7) 17892
(8) 13725
(9) 17451
(10) 21306
(11) 9724
(12) 12765

Exercise 73
(1) 8874
(2) 12985
(3) 15192
(4) 19610
(5) 23256
(6) 29250
(7) 34440
(8) 40740
(9) 12926
(10) 17954
(11) 20832
(12) 26877

Exercise 74
(1) 31980
(2) 39985
(3) 47823
(4) 54634
(5) 14756
(6) 23920
(7) 30492
(8) 37275
(9) 49421
(10) 55286
(11) 65754
(12) 77815

Exercise 75
(1) 7216
(2) 7830
(3) 6992
(4) 10951
(5) 10320
(6) 7497
(7) 8200
(8) 8996
(9) 10304
(10) 10602
(11) 7946
(12) 7869

Exercise 76
(1) 13516
(2) 16705
(3) 17353
(4) 10764
(5) 11376
(6) 42600
(7) 56772
(8) 58725
(9) 72791
(10) 79866
(11) 74184
(12) 69865

Exercise 77
(1) 90334
(2) 74035
(3) 54872
(4) 48510
(5) 71456
(6) 74250
(7) 59490
(8) 79540
(9) 59356
(10) 66154
(11) 82192
(12) 58717

Exercise 78
(1) 74980
(2) 61795
(3) 49203
(4) 73154
(5) 68716
(6) 72960
(7) 49932
(8) 66825
(9) 90861
(10) 62986
(11) 65384
(12) 67815

Exercise 79
(1) 11.2
(2) 81.1
(3) 55.44
(4) 239.69
(5) 0.8
(6) 8.8
(7) 6.9
(8) 15.72
(9) 25.6
(10) 39.48
(11) 132.1
(12) 632.08
(13) 2.11
(14) 18.8
(15) 2.04
(16) 1.2
(17) £6.46
(18) £9.55
(19) £7.05
(20) £1.15

ANSWERS

(21) 2m80cm
(22) 150cm
(23) 6m80cm
(24) 15cm
(25) 248kg982g
(26) 1.301kg
(27) 1kg686g
(28) 750g
(29) 1L280ml
(30) 800ml
(31) 4L375ml
(32) 800ml
(33) 2hrs19min
(34) 2hrs42min
(35) 2hrs30min
(36) 0hrs27min
(37) 3120
(38) 1807
(39) 6838
(40) 6136

Exercise 80

(1) 15.2
(2) 94.6
(3) 144.41
(4) 303.18
(5) 1.7
(6) 10.2
(7) 94.9
(8) 57.72
(9) 49.2
(10) 78.96
(11) 311.04
(12) 760.72
(13) 1.05
(14) 9.92
(15) 3.23
(16) 1.6
(17) £14.49
(18) £11.60
(19) £47.95
(20) £0.35
(21) 5m70cm
(22) 8750cm
(23) 1m44cm
(24) 19cm
(25) 678kg999g
(26) 6.001kg
(27) 3kg572g
(28) 1500g
(29) 3L560ml
(30) 1800ml
(31) 3L400ml
(32) 600ml
(33) 3hrs2min
(34) 3hrs3min
(35) 3hrs4min
(36) 1hr27min
(37) 8064
(38) 11790
(39) 6912
(40) 16014

Exercise 81

(1) 16.3
(2) 112.9
(3) 157.94
(4) 135.17
(5) 3.1
(6) 6.8
(7) 92.5
(8) 69.43
(9) 57.4
(10) 39.76
(11) 313.68
(12) 465.05
(13) 0.43
(14) 11.6
(15) 3.11
(16) 1.6
(17) £17.36
(18) £2.35
(19) £27
(20) £1.67
(21) 5m67cm
(22) 3340cm
(23) 3m6cm
(24) 19cm
(25) 278kg777g
(26) 8.241kg
(27) 4kg460g
(28) 1750g
(29) 8L670ml
(30) 5200ml
(31) 5L838ml
(32) 1400ml
(33) 3hrs6min
(34) 8hrs26min
(35) 12hrs24min
(36) 1hr28min
(37) 6192
(38) 5364
(39) 17248
(40) 38454

Exercise 82

(1) 17.6
(2) 150
(3) 119.11
(4) 266.72
(5) 1.8
(6) 1.8
(7) 60.9
(8) 7.77
(9) 50.4
(10) 46.1
(11) 202.26
(12) 807.39
(13) 1.07
(14) 14.6
(15) 4.71
(16) 1.8
(17) £13.56
(18) £18.03
(19) £58.80
(20) £16.35
(21) 4m67cm
(22) 850cm
(23) 2m45cm
(24) 35cm
(25) 548kg882g
(26) 5.501kg
(27) 2kg664g
(28) 2250g
(29) 7L270ml
(30) 2200ml
(31) 2L952ml
(32) 1800ml
(33) 1hr48min
(34) 6hrs34min
(35) 6hrs32min
(36) 1hr27min
(37) 58110
(38) 61831
(39) 78795
(40) 98802

Exercise 83

(1) 12
(2) 148.1
(3) 101.14
(4) 999.49
(5) 8.7
(6) 14.2
(7) 1127.9
(8) 42.72
(9) 76
(10) 34.83
(11) 253.12
(12) 909.81
(13) 12.76
(14) 9.3
(15) 4.56
(16) 1.8
(17) £139.79
(18) £158.70
(19) £481.95
(20) £2.15
(21) 7m77cm
(22) 1cm
(23) 6m84cm
(24) 21cm
(25) 342kg229g
(26) 3.767kg
(27) 6kg558g
(28) 15000g
(29) 9L960ml
(30) 300ml
(31) 7L425ml
(32) 1800ml
(33) 4hrs19min
(34) 8hrs3min
(35) 5hrs29min
(36) 1hr34min
(37) 84681
(38) 47925
(39) 63963
(40) 86652

Exercise 84

(1) 26.1
(2) 482.9
(3) 258.94
(4) 236.27
(5) 6.1
(6) 26.8
(7) 56.5
(8) 66.43
(9) 145.6
(10) 569.82
(11) 1427.36
(12) 264.06
(13) 1.81
(14) 111.6
(15) 23.03
(16) 2.8
(17) £181.36
(18) £25.35
(19) £271
(20) £17.27
(21) 15m167cm
(22) 1740cm
(23) 5m4cm
(24) 15cm
(25) 348kg567g
(26) 7.541kg
(27) 4kg452g
(28) 4250g
(29) 10L670ml
(30) 1400ml
(31) 8L406ml
(32) 3500ml
(33) 19hrs20min
(34) 9hrs45min
(35) 31hrs20min
(36) 1hr4min
(37) 35948
(38) 69888
(39) 54535
(40) 24418

Exercise 85

(1) 16
(2) 130.1
(3) 131.14
(4) 239.49
(5) 7.7
(6) 6.7
(7) 3131.9
(8) 24.72
(9) 31.5
(10) 50.16
(11) 288.96
(12) 891.81
(13) 5.73
(14) 17.91
(15) 10.73
(16) 1.6
(17) £224.19
(18) £502.7
(19) £5462.8
(20) £9.55
(21) 17m7cm
(22) 1444cm
(23) 2m88cm
(24) 11cm
(25) 366kg211g
(26) 7.468kg
(27) 12kg355g
(28) 80,000g
(29) 7L660ml
(30) 100ml
(31) 6L984ml
(32) 1400ml
(33) 3hrs27min
(34) 5hrs6min
(35) 4hrs30min
(36) 1hr25min
(37) 32091
(38) 76415
(39) 67373
(40) 78848

Exercise 86

(1) 24.1
(2) 309.9
(3) 411.94
(4) 78.47
(5) 35
(6) 10.5
(7) 206.5
(8) 29.39
(9) 262.8
(10) 620.69
(11) 3315.78
(12) 342.37
(13) 2.0675
(14) 61.1
(15) 8.08
(16) 3.6
(17) £351.36
(18) £42.65
(19) £355
(20) £31.27
(21) 19m897cm
(22) 113cm
(23) 3m84cm
(24) 18cm
(25) 875kg293g
(26) 5.401kg
(27) 5kg328g
(28) 2375g
(29) 6L670ml
(30) 1100ml
(31) 3L948ml
(32) 2700ml
(33) 14hrs10min
(34) 14hrs35min
(35) 27hrs45min
(36) 1hr36min
(37) 87048
(38) 61161
(39) 22610
(40) 69362